the GRACE *and* TRUTH PARADOX

RANDY ALCORN

Learning Activities and Leader Guide
by Debbie Kubik Evert

LifeWay Press®
Nashville, Tennessee

ISBN 0-6331-9755-6

This book is a resource for course CG-1052 in the Personal Life category of the Christian Growth Study Plan.

Dewey Decimal Classification: 248.84
Subject Headings: CHRISTIAN LIFE \ GRACE (THEOLOGY) \ TRUTH

Photography:
Grand Canyon: David Noton Photography/Alamy
Inset: Michael Gomez

Unless otherwise noted, all Scripture quotations are taken from the Holman Christian Standard Bible®, copyright © 1999, 2000, 2001, 2002, 2003 by Holman Bible Publishers. Used by permission.

Scripture quotations identified NIV are from the Holy Bible, New International Version, copyright © 1973, 1978, 1984 by International Bible Society. Used by permission.

Scripture quotations identified NASB are taken from the NEW AMERICAN STANDARD BIBLE, © Copyright 1960, 1962, 1963, 1968, 1971, 1972, 1973, 1975, 1977, 1995. Used by permission.

To order additional copies of this resource: WRITE to LifeWay Church Resources Customer Service; One LifeWay Plaza; Nashville, TN 37234-0113; FAX (615) 251-5933; PHONE toll free (800) 458-2772; E-MAIL *customerservice@lifeway.com;* ORDER ONLINE at *www.lifeway.com;* or VISIT the LifeWay Christian Store serving you.

Printed in the United States of America

Leadership and Adult Publishing
LifeWay Church Resources
One LifeWay Plaza
Nashville, TN 37234-0175

Contents

About the Author

Randy Alcorn, a former pastor and a best-selling author, is the founder and director of Eternal Perspective Ministries (EPM), a nonprofit organization dedicated to teaching biblical truth and drawing attention to the needy. EPM exists to meet the needs of the unreached, unfed, unborn, uneducated, unreconciled, and unsupported people around the world. "My ministry focus is communicating the strategic importance of using our earthly time, money, possessions, and opportunities to invest in need-meeting ministries that count for eternity," Alcorn says. "I do that by trying to analyze, teach, and apply the implications of Christian truth."

Alcorn's novels include *Deadline, Dominion, Edge of Eternity, Lord Foulgrin's Letters, The Ishbane Conspiracy,* and *Safely Home.* His nonfiction books include *The Treasure Principle; The Purity Principle; In Light of Eternity; ProLife Answers to ProChoice Arguments; Money, Possessions, and Eternity;* and *Heaven.*

Alcorn attended Multnomah Bible College and Western Seminary, where he received his bachelor of theology, master of arts in biblical studies, and doctor of divinity. He and his wife, Nanci, live in Gresham, Oregon, and have two married daughters, Karina Franklin and Angela Stump.

A paradox is a statement or a phrase that seems to contradict itself but, in fact, is true. One of the greatest paradoxes of the Christian faith is the interplay between grace and truth. Grace, by itself, may permit deception and moral compromise. Truth, by itself, leads to self-righteousness and crushing legalism. Are these two qualities mutually exclusive?

Jesus' life demonstrated that grace and truth can coexist. In fact, He expressed them in perfect balance, showing that God's absolute truth cannot be compromised and His amazing grace cannot be denied. The Bible describes Jesus as "full of grace and truth" (John 1:14).

The challenge for believers today is how to express grace and truth in balance, as Jesus did. It's an important issue because the world will draw conclusions about Jesus from what it sees in us. If we fail the truth test, people won't see Jesus. If we fail the grace test, people won't see Jesus. Only by expressing both qualities in balance can we accurately show Christ's character to the world.

This study will teach you the meanings of *grace* and *truth* as revealed in God's Word and will illustrate the way Jesus balanced these qualities as He brought redemption and healing to people. You will discover your tendency to express either grace or truth, and you will learn how to maintain a better balance in your life. By learning to show grace and truth, you can reflect Jesus' character as you offer others both the hope and the need for salvation in Him.

week 1

day 1

Two Foundational Concepts

Case in Point

For most of today's lesson you will read a story that really
happened to me. It illustrates the heart of this study.

Late one rainy night my wife and I were leaving a movie
theater when Nanci noticed an older man in the parking lot
leaning on a walker and struggling. I helped him get into his
car. Because he was exhausted, I asked if I could drive him
home. He declined, but I said we would follow him home in
case he needed help. As he pulled out of his parking place,
driving erratically, we prayed he wouldn't find the street. Our
prayers were answered when he got trapped in a fast-food
drive-through line. I opened his door and asked him to move
to the passenger seat so that I could drive him home, while
Nanci followed.

As I pulled out, two men jumped in front of the car,
waving their arms and a cell phone. One shouted, "My wife's
having our baby, and I have to get home! Can you drive us?"

"Well," I said, "this isn't my car, and I don't know this man
sitting next to me." Sounded pretty lame, don't you think? Keep
reading. It gets better.

I asked Nanci to drive the older man's car and follow me while I took the guys home (wherever that was). After dropping them off, I hopped back in with George—by now I knew his name—to take him home (wherever that was). When we reached his place, I helped him to his room.

I found out that George had been a political-science professor at San Francisco State University for 28 years. I realized that most people of George's background would not count Bible-believing Christians among their favorite people! George asked me why we had helped him. I told him we that are followers of Christ, and I left him my book *In Light of Eternity*. I prayed that God would touch his life, and I hoped we'd hear the rest of the story in eternity. As it turns out, we didn't have to wait that long.

Two months later my assistant, Kathy, woke up in the middle of the night experiencing a strange medical problem she'd never had before and hasn't had since. The next day she went to her doctor, taking with her a copy of *In Light of Eternity*. When the doctor saw it, he said, "One of my patients was carrying that book the other day, and he told me he wished he could talk to the author."

Kathy returned to our office with George's phone number. I called George and asked whether he wanted me to drop by. He did. George was full of questions. He wanted to know the truth about Jesus Christ. He couldn't get over the idea of grace, that God could really forgive rotten people. He said it sounded too easy.

Two hours of discussion followed. I saw God's Spirit at work in George. Finally he prayed, confessed his sin, and accepted Christ's gift of eternal life.

Now what are the chances of all these events coinciding? No chance at all. They were a series of divine appointments! A small act of grace by my wife and me (two small acts, counting the trip to the woman having a baby) somehow made an impression on George and placed into his hands a book that offered him the truth.

What was it that George saw, wrestled with, and ultimately brought him to Christ? Grace and truth. These are the qualities that give believers away.

A friend sat down in a small London restaurant and picked up a menu. "What will it be?" the waiter asked.

Studying the puzzling selections, my friend muttered, "Uhh ..."

The waiter smiled. "Oh, a Yank. What part of the States are you from?"

Although my friend hadn't said a word, he had already given himself away. In the first century Christ's followers were also recognized immediately. What gave them away?

It wasn't their buildings. They had none.

It wasn't their programs. They had none.

It wasn't their political power. They had none.

It wasn't their slick publications, TV networks, bumper stickers, or celebrities. They had none.

What made the early believers stand out? You can discover what it was by reading a passage from a book that tells the story of the first-century church.

Read Acts 4:32-33.

THE MULTITUDE OF THOSE WHO BELIEVED WERE OF ONE HEART AND SOUL, AND NO ONE SAID THAT ANY OF HIS POSSESSIONS WAS HIS OWN, BUT INSTEAD THEY HELD EVERYTHING IN COMMON. AND WITH GREAT POWER THE APOSTLES WERE GIVING TESTIMONY TO THE RESURRECTION OF THE LORD JESUS, AND GREAT GRACE WAS ON ALL OF THEM. *ACTS 4:32-33*

**What actions made
the early believers easily recognizable?**

_____

_____

_____

The early believers testified to the truth about Christ and lived by His grace. Truth was the food they ate and the message they spoke. Grace was the air they breathed and the life they lived. The world around the first-century Christians had never seen anything like them. It still hasn't.

How closely would you say that you follow the early church's example?

No resemblance   A partial resemblance   A close resemblance

In what ways is your church similar to this early church?

_____

_____

_____

Remember, no church is perfect, because it is made up of humans. So be gentle in evaluating your church. On the other hand, where you see an area to improve, pray for your church's leaders and members to seek God's heart and to have His priorities. Also pray that you will be the church member God wants you to be.

Let's take a moment to clarify what I mean by grace and truth. Grace isn't good manners, and by truth I don't just mean speaking honestly.

Truth refers to the legal demands on humanity that God's character requires and the absolute law He established in His Word. God's holiness, justice, and wrath are expressions of His truth. The fact that God hates sin and judges sin illustrates the integrity of His character and the uncompromising demands of His truth.

Grace, on the other hand, is the aspect of God's character that overrides His judgment of our sin. God's grace led Him to sacrifice His Son to pay the penalty for our sin, offering all people an opportunity to be forgiven and to have new life in Christ. God's love and the good news of Jesus Christ are examples of the grace God extends to us.

Categorize each of the following words as describing either grace or truth.

Law	❑ Grace	❑ Truth
Forgiveness	❑ Grace	❑ Truth
Mercy	❑ Grace	❑ Truth
Obedience	❑ Grace	❑ Truth
Wrath	❑ Grace	❑ Truth
Justice	❑ Grace	❑ Truth
Gospel	❑ Grace	❑ Truth
Love	❑ Grace	❑ Truth

THE DAY IN REVIEW

Review today's lesson. What was the most important concept you read today?

_____

_____

How will this truth challenge you to be like Christ?

_____

_____

_____

Pray, asking God to help you begin to understand the concepts of grace and truth. Write your prayer below.

_____

_____

_____

_____

_____

Two Essential Characteristics

The only church-growth formula first-century Christians had was the body of truth flowing with the blood of grace. They drew thousands to Jesus by being like Jesus. But what does it mean to be like Jesus?

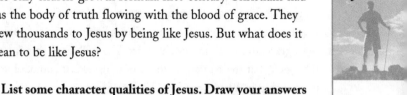

List some character qualities of Jesus. Draw your answers from what you have heard and have been taught.

_____   _____   _____

_____   _____   _____

Actually, we could make a long list of Jesus' qualities. But the longer the list, the less we could wrap our minds around it. But what if Christ's character could be reduced to two ingredients? In fact, it can be. We find these qualities in John 1:1,14.

IN THE BEGINNING WAS THE WORD;
AND THE WORD WAS WITH GOD,
AND THE WORD WAS GOD.
THE WORD BECAME FLESH
AND TOOK UP RESIDENCE AMONG US.
WE OBSERVED HIS GLORY,
THE GLORY AS THE ONE AND ONLY SON FROM THE FATHER,
FULL OF GRACE AND TRUTH. *JOHN 1:1,14*

The two qualities are _____ **and** _____.

Not "full of patience, wisdom, beauty, compassion, and creativity." Yes, He had these characteristics, but Scripture distills Christ's attributes into a two-point checklist of Christlikeness: grace and truth. John 1:14 says Jesus came "from the Father, full of grace and truth." Verse 17 says, "Grace and truth came through Jesus Christ."

People today should have only to look at us to see what Jesus is like. For better or worse, they will draw conclusions about Christ from what they see in us. If we fail the grace test, we fail to be Christlike. If we fail the truth test, we fail to be Christlike. If we pass both tests, we are like Jesus.

Because we as believers have Christ living in us, we possess both grace and truth in our character. You will learn throughout this book that these qualities form an unusual but compatible relationship in a believer's life. Wherever you are on this journey with Christ, it is important for you to discover your tendencies toward grace and truth.

On the scale below place a *G* to indicate how you reflect grace in your life. Use these criteria:

0: I don't show grace to others or myself. I am better at pointing out flaws.

25: I think about showing grace to others, but I find myself being judgmental.

50: I show grace to others and myself most of the time, but I still can't offer forgiveness in some situations.

75: I study Scripture—especially about the way Christ responded to others—and seek to be as loving as He is.

100: I can love people no matter what they have done.

0	25	50	75	100

Now go back and mark how you reflect truth in your life by placing a *T* on the scale. Use these criteria:

0: I seldom stand up for truth, because I don't want to hurt anybody's feelings.

25: I am learning that truth is best, but it's really difficult to be consistent.

50: I've asked a couple of Christian friends to hold me accountable to live up to the truth I profess. And they do!

75: I'm becoming more willing to confront others and myself to stand up for what is right. Obedience to Christ is more important than pleasing people.

100: I insist on living up to the Bible's standards of righteousness. A grace-starved, truth-starved world needs Jesus, full of grace and truth. What does this hungry world see when it looks at us?

How would someone describe Christ according to what they see in you? Circle a word in each pair.

Haughty or humble?   Judgmental or forgiving?
Selfish or selfless?   Demanding or gentle?
Impatient or patient?   Legalistic or gracious?
Compromising or unwavering?   Loving or angry?

THE DAY IN REVIEW

Review today's lesson. What was the most important concept you read today?

_____

_____

How will this truth challenge you to be like Christ?

_____

_____

Pray, asking God to help you be more like Christ, especially as you seek to show grace and share truth with others. Write your prayer below.

_____

_____

_____

_____

_____

A Balancing Act

day 3

Like individuals, some churches today embrace truth but need a heavy dose of grace. Other churches talk about grace but cry out for a heavy dose of truth. Let me illustrate with this story.

I invited a lesbian activist to lunch. For the first hour she hammered me, telling of all the Christians who had mistreated her. She seemed as hard as nails. I listened, trying to show her God's grace, praying that she would see the Jesus she desperately needed. She raised her voice and cursed freely. People stared. But that was OK. Jesus went to the cross for her; the least I could do was listen.

Suddenly she was crying, sobbing, broken. I reached across the table and took her hand. For the next two hours I listened to her story, her heartsickness, her doubts about the causes she championed. And I told her about Christ's grace.

After four hours we walked out of that restaurant, side by side. We hugged.

Check which was expressed: ❑ Grace ❑ Truth ❑ Both

In our conversation truth wasn't shared at the expense of grace or grace at the expense of truth. Both were shared. It's exactly what this young woman needed to experience.

Stop for a minute. From what you've read, do grace and truth seem to be opposites? ❑ Yes ❑ No

At times grace and truth might seem to be polar opposites, not even in the same room or on the same planet! Are grace and truth compatible? Can they coexist?

The apparent conflict between grace and truth isn't because they are incompatible but because we lack perspective to resolve their paradox. The two are interdependent. We should never approach truth except in a spirit of grace or grace except in a spirit of truth. Just as Jesus wasn't 50 percent human and 50 percent divine, He wasn't 50 percent grace and 50 percent truth. Jesus was 100 percent grace and 100 percent truth.

Read the following accounts of Jesus' life and mark whether they express grace, truth, or both.

Matthew 8:18-22:	❏ Grace	❏ Truth	❏ Both
Matthew 12:1-8:	❏ Grace	❏ Truth	❏ Both
Matthew 19:16-22:	❏ Grace	❏ Truth	❏ Both
Matthew 20:1-16:	❏ Grace	❏ Truth	❏ Both
Matthew 21:18-22:	❏ Grace	❏ Truth	❏ Both

Some of the answers might not seem obvious. You'll have a chance to discuss them with your group.

While Jesus kept a perfect balance between grace and truth, believers today may find it easier to express either one or the other. Truth-oriented Christians love studying Scripture and theology. But sometimes they are quick to judge and slow to forgive. They are strong on truth, weak on grace.

Grace-oriented Christians love forgiveness and freedom. But sometimes they neglect biblical study and see moral standards as legalism. They are strong on grace, weak on truth.

Countless mistakes in relationships and ministry are caused by failures to balance grace and truth. Sometimes we neglect both. Often we choose one over the other.

After each example indicate whether the person is oriented more toward expressions of grace or truth.

Madeleine has found that when she studies the Bible, she feels convicted to confront others with their disobedience to God. But because she doesn't want to be rejected, she has decided not to study the Bible but just to love others without trying to impose her values on them.

Which quality predominates?   ❏ Grace   ❏ Truth

15

Terry studies the Bible and theology to make certain he doesn't break any biblical directives. Terry's legalistic leanings make it hard for him to accept other people's faults and to forgive their shortcomings.

Which quality predominates? ❑ Grace ❑ Truth

It's obvious that Madeleine emphasizes grace over truth, while Terry overemphasizes truth at the expense of grace. Like Jesus, we need to exercise both qualities in balance.

This challenge reminds me of Moses, our Dalmatian. When one tennis ball is in his mouth, the other is on the floor. When he goes for the second ball, he drops the first. Large dogs can get two balls in their mouths. Not Moses. He manages to get two in his mouth only momentarily. To his distress, one ball or the other spurts out onto the floor.

Similarly, our minds don't seem big enough to hold on to grace and truth at the same time. We go after the grace ball, only to drop the truth ball to make room for it. We need to stretch our undersized minds to hold them both at once.

How do you think an overemphasis on grace or truth affects believers' witness?

Truth without grace: _____

_____

_____

Grace without truth: _____

_____

_____

Truth without grace breeds a self-righteous legalism that poisons the church and pushes the world from Christ. Grace without truth breeds moral indifference and keeps people from seeing their need for Christ. It's not enough for us to offer grace or truth. We must offer both. That's what this study is about.

THE DAY IN REVIEW

**Review today's lesson. What was the most important
concept you read today?**

_____

_____

_____

_____

How will this truth challenge you to be like Christ?

_____

_____

_____

_____

**Pray, asking God to help you balance grace and truth
and to show both. Also ask for help to grow
in both areas. Write your prayer below.**

_____

_____

_____

_____

_____

_____

_____

_____

_____

Spiritual Symmetry

day 4

Our DNA's double helix is perfectly balanced at life's core. Two strands wrap around each other, forming an axis of symmetry. The two strands run in opposite directions, providing perfect correction for each other.

Grace and truth are like spiritual DNA. They are the building blocks of Christ-centered living. These complementary strands create flawless spiritual balance and stability. Though the strands run in opposite directions, they correspond perfectly. Without both strands we cannot function properly.

**Below you see a drawing of a DNA chain.
Mark one strand *Grace* and the other *Truth* to picture
the way these strands weave together to create a balance.**

The trick is finding that perfect balance. It isn't always easy. Believe me, I know.

In 1989 and 1990 I intervened—peacefully and nonviolently— on behalf of unborn children at abortion clinics. As a result, I was arrested several times and was sent to jail for a few days.

I don't regret what I did; I still believe unborn children are precious to their Creator. That truth compelled me to say and do things that proved unpopular—among non-Christians and Christians alike. I reasoned that because these really are children—not just potential children—they need people to

> Speak up for those who have no voice,
> for the justice of all who are dispossessed.
> Speak up, judge righteously,
> and defend the cause of the oppressed
> and needy. *Proverbs 31:8-9*

Responding to the issue of abortion demonstrates
❑ grace   ❑ truth.

What got me in trouble was attempting to honor both truth
and grace. You see, while speaking the truth about abortion,
I also felt compelled to show grace to unbelievers. I never
shouted, jeered, or did anything demeaning. I never raised
my voice, touched anyone, or said anything unkind. Alongside
others I sought to share Christ's grace at abortion clinics.
(One person came to Christ right outside the clinic door.)

**Showing Christ's character to abortion proponents
demonstrates** ❑ grace   ❑ truth.

Let's consider the way Jesus saw His ministry of grace and
truth. Jesus summed up His mission on earth in Luke 4:16-21.

**Read Luke 4:16-21 from your Bible. Finish the phrases
below that tell what Jesus did while on earth.**

_____ to the poor
_____ to the captives
_____ to the blind
_____ the oppressed
_____ the year of the Lord's favor

Jesus did not come to minister to those who had everything.
Jesus came to serve those who could not serve themselves.
And He did it with grace and truth in perfect balance.

A few years ago the church I used to pastor and still attend
was picketed by 30 protesters. Why? Some of our members go
to abortion clinics and offer alternatives, sharing the gospel
when they can. Sometimes they hold up signs saying, Consider
Adoption, Let Your Baby Live, and We'll Help Financially.

Three proabortion groups decided to join forces and give
our church a taste of our own medicine. On a rainy Sunday
morning our church parking lot was invaded by Radical

Women for Choice, Rock for Choice, and the Lesbian Avengers. Having heard they were coming, we set out donuts and coffee. I spent 1½ hours with a protester named Charles, who held a sign saying, Keep Abortion Legal.

We talked a little about abortion and a lot about Christ. I explained the gospel. He gave me his address. Later I sent him some Christian literature.

I liked Charles. But when you believe as I do that abortion is killing children, it's a bit awkward serving coffee and holding an umbrella for someone waving a proabortion sign. If you don't understand, imagine doing that for someone holding a sign declaring, Legalize Rape or Kill Minorities. Yet because of the opportunity to share Christ's grace, it seemed right.

What is your reaction to what the church members did?

_____

_____

_____

It's not just truth that puts us in awkward situations. So does grace.

On the morning we were picketed, some street preachers showed up to take on the abortion activists with signs threatening hell and damnation. Their message contained truth, but their approach lacked grace. One of the street preachers barged between my daughter and me and a few Lesbian Avengers just as we finally had an opportunity to talk with them. The door of witnessing was slammed in our face—by Christian brothers.

We tried to reason with the street preachers. After all, this was our church, and we didn't want them screaming at our "guests," even if they were screaming truth. Most cooperated, but a few decided we were compromising truth and it was an abomination for us to offer donuts to people who needed to be rebuked.

What could the street preachers have done differently to show grace in addition to truth? _____

_____

The following Sunday, two street preachers picketed our church, scolding us for our "pathetic" attempts at donut-and-coffee evangelism.

    How would you have responded to these picketers?

_____

_____

    How would your response have shown grace?

_____

_____

    How would your response have shown truth?

_____

_____

After 21 years without being picketed, our church was picketed two weeks in a row—first by radically liberal nonbelievers for speaking truth and second by radically conservative believers for showing grace.

That's how it is on this tightrope walk between truth and grace. When you stand for truth, you are held in contempt by some non-Christians (and even some Christians). When you try to demonstrate grace, you're held in contempt by some Christians (and even some non-Christians). When you try to live by grace and truth, in some eyes you'll be too radical; in other eyes, not radical enough.

So we have to make a choice. Are we going to spend our lives trying to please the grace-haters or the truth-haters (see John 15:18)? Or are we going to seek to please the only One whose judgment seat we will stand before—Jesus, who is full of grace and truth?

THE DAY IN REVIEW

**Review today's lesson. What was the most important
concept you read today?**

_____

_____

_____

_____

_____

How will this truth challenge you to be like Christ?

_____

_____

_____

_____

**Pray, asking God to help you stand for truth even when it
compels you to say and do things that might be unpopular—
among non-Christians and Christians alike. Also ask Him
to help you demonstrate grace when you confront others
with the truth. Write your prayer below.**

_____

_____

_____

_____

_____

_____

_____

_____

_____

_____

_____

_____

A Lion or a Lamb?

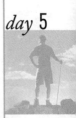

Something is wrong if all unbelievers like us. Something is wrong if all unbelievers hate us. If we accurately demonstrate grace and truth, some people will be drawn to us, and others will be offended—just as they were by Jesus.

When we offend everyone, it's because we've taken on the truth mantle without grace. When we offend no one, it's because we've watered down truth in the name of grace.

Read the following scene from *The Lion, the Witch, and the Wardrobe* from C. S. Lewis's *Chronicles of Narnia* series. In this scene Susan asks Mr. and Mrs. Beaver about Aslan the Lion:

"Is he—quite safe? I shall feel rather nervous about meeting a lion."

"That you will, Dearie, and no mistake," said Mrs. Beaver. "If there's anyone who can appear before Aslan without their knees knocking, they're either braver than most or just plain silly."

"Then he isn't safe?" said Lucy.

"Safe?" said Mrs. Beaver. "Don't you hear what Mrs. Beaver tells you? Who said anything about safe? Of course he isn't safe. But he's good. He's the King, I tell you."[1]

Christ is good. But until we understand that He's not safe, until we come to grips with the truth of His uncompromising holiness, we will never begin to grasp His grace.

Have you ever thought of Jesus as not being safe?
❑ Yes   ❑ No

Explain in your own words what you think that means.

_____

_____

_____

Many people today try to reinvent Jesus, giving Him a facelift. They spin His statements for public consumption, making Him fit into popular notions of the kind of Christ people want. But He's notoriously uncooperative with all attempts at repackaging and marketing. He's not looking for image-enhancers. We are to follow Him as servants, not walk in front of him as a public-relations entourage.

How have you heard or seen Jesus marketed in our society?

**If you can't think of anything now, notice
bumper stickers the next time you are on the road.
Write down what you see.**

Many people didn't recognize Jesus when He walked on earth. They were looking for the Messiah as a powerful lion, bringing judgment on His enemies. But they overlooked Scripture passages showing that He would come as a lamb.

**Read Isaiah 53:7 and circle the words that tell
how the lamb (or sheep) responded.**

HE WAS OPPRESSED AND AFFLICTED,
YET HE DID NOT OPEN HIS MOUTH.
LIKE A LAMB LED TO THE SLAUGHTER
AND LIKE A SHEEP SILENT BEFORE HER SHEARERS,
HE DID NOT OPEN HIS MOUTH. *ISAIAH 53:7*

The Book of Revelation prophesies that the Lamb will appear "like a slaughtered lamb" (Rev. 5:6). This seems to be a picture of weakness, but one chapter later people hide themselves from the "wrath of the Lamb" (Rev. 6:16). Toward the end of this exciting Book we read, "These will make war against the Lamb, but the Lamb will conquer them because He is Lord of lords and King of kings" (17:14). Not exactly words of weakness.

Let's revisit the children in C. S. Lewis's *Narnia* series. At the end of *The Voyage of the Dawn Treader* the children see a bright white lamb speaking in a "sweet milky voice."[2] As they talk, suddenly "his snowy white flushed into tawny gold and his size changed and he was Aslan himself, towering above them and scattering light from his mane."[3] The Lamb of grace is the Lion of truth.

Sometimes we see Him as one, sometimes as the other. He is always both.

THE DAY IN REVIEW

Review today's lesson. What was the most important concept you read today?

_____

_____

How will this truth challenge you to be like Christ?

_____

_____

Pray, asking God to help you be as strong as the Lion of truth and as gentle as the Lamb of grace. Write your prayer below.

_____

_____

_____

_____

---

[1] *The Lion, the Witch and the Wardrobe* by C. S. Lewis copyright © C. S. Lewis Pte. Ltd. 1950. Extract reprinted by permission.
[2] *The Voyage of the Dawn Treader* by C. S. Lewis copyright © C. S. Lewis Pte. Ltd. 1952. Extract reprinted by permission.
[3] Ibid. Extract reprinted by permission.

week 2

What Is Grace?

day 1

A Wretch like Whom?

Before I spoke at a conference, a soloist sang one of my favorite songs, "Amazing Grace." It was beautiful. Until she got to the 10th word.

> Amazing grace! how sweet the sound,
> That saved a [soul] like me![1]

My heart sank when I heard that the word *wretch* had been edited out! I thought about John Newton, the songwriter. This former slave trader, guilty of the vilest sins, knew that he was a wretch. That's exactly what made God's grace so amazing. Mind-boggling. Knockdown awesome.

Look up the word *wretch* in a dictionary. Write its definition.

_____

_____

Here's what Webster says: "a miserable person: one who is profoundly unhappy or in great misfortune; a base, despicable, or vile person." Words in the definition also include "deeply afflicted, dejected, or distressed; ... deplorably bad; being or appearing mean, miserable, or contemptible; ... inferior."[2]

Not very nice words. Not a good condition to be in either. Would you want to hang around someone you considered a wretch or with someone who acted wretched? Jesus did (see Rom. 5:6). That's grace!

WHILE WE WERE STILL HELPLESS, AT THE APPOINTED MOMENT, CHRIST DIED FOR THE UNGODLY. *ROMANS 5:6*

Ungodly. That's deeper than just miserable or unpleasant. Like *wretched,* not a word you'd want to use to describe yourself. But that was our condition before Christ's sacrifice.

Before grace, that is.

Consider a story about grace. In 1987 18-month-old Baby Jessica fell 22 feet into a Texas well. Rescuers labored nonstop to save her. After 55 grueling hours as her life hung in the balance, they finally reached her and extracted her from the well. The nation breathed a sigh of relief and cheered the heroes.

But what if the story went something like this? "Baby Jessica clawed her 18-month-old body up the side of that well, inch by inch, digging in her little toes and working her way up. She's a hero, that Jessica!"

How would that scenario change the message of grace?

_____

_____

_____

That's not the way it happened. Baby Jessica was utterly helpless. Her fate was in the hands of her rescuers. Left to herself, Jessica had no chance. Sound familiar? When it comes to our salvation, we're utterly helpless, absolutely powerless. We get no more applause for our redemption than Baby Jessica got for being rescued. God alone deserves the ovation. In the story of redemption He is the only hero. And it didn't just cost Him 55 hours of hard work. It cost Him everything.

If we're nothing more than morally neutral souls, as expressed in the revised hymn I heard, think about the implications. It guts grace. The better we are, the less we need grace. The more we can do for ourselves, the less we need someone to help. Grace becomes less amazing.

Although not perfect, an 18-month-old child hasn't had much time to do evil things, to be a wretch. She's innocent. But change Baby Jessica in the story to Osama bin Laden, and you have a better picture of redemption.

**Change the character in the story to Osama bin Laden.
How would you feel if he were rescued from a well?**

_____

_____

**How can God offer the same grace to someone
who is not innocent, like Hitler or Stalin?**

_____

_____

The Bible makes an astounding proclamation in Romans 5:8.

GOD PROVES HIS OWN LOVE FOR US IN THAT WHILE WE WERE
STILL SINNERS CHRIST DIED FOR US! *ROMANS 5:8*

What was our condition when Christ died for us?

_____

"While we were still sinners." The verse doesn't say that we had to change or clean up our act before God would deliver us. Sinners. Helpless sinners. Wretched. Ungodly. Desperate for deliverance. Our spiritual condition without Christ is complete helplessness.

Some argue that people are basically good and do not need a Savior. If we aren't so bad without Christ, then why did He have to endure the cross?

Read Galatians 2:21 and complete the sentence:
If people are good enough, _____.

IF RIGHTEOUSNESS COMES THROUGH THE LAW, THEN
CHRIST DIED FOR NOTHING. *GALATIANS 2:21*

Paul said if people are good enough, "then Christ died for nothing." Christ gave His all to save us all. That's grace. Period.

Grace never ignores the awful truth of our depravity. In fact, grace emphasizes this fact. The worse we realize we are, the greater we realize God's grace is.

Grace isn't about God lowering His standards. It's about God fulfilling those standards through the substitutionary suffering of the One who set the standards. Christ went to the cross because He would not ignore the truths of His holiness and our sin. Grace gave what truth demanded: the ultimate sacrifice for our sins.

Read 2 Corinthians 5:21, another verse about Christ's sacrifice.

HE [GOD] MADE THE ONE WHO DID NOT KNOW SIN TO BE SIN FOR US,
SO THAT WE MIGHT BECOME THE RIGHTEOUSNESS OF GOD IN HIM.
2 CORINTHIANS 5:21

What does the verse say happened to Jesus?

_____

Why did Christ become sin?

_____

Accepting the truth of human depravity may be a blow, but grasping this doctrine is liberating. Why? Read Isaiah 64:6.

ALL OF US HAVE BECOME LIKE ONE WHO IS UNCLEAN,
AND ALL OUR RIGHTEOUS ACTS ARE LIKE FILTHY RAGS. *ISAIAH 64:6, NIV*

When I realize the best I can do without Him is like filthy rags in His sight, it finally sinks in that I have nothing to offer. Salvation therefore hinges on His work, not mine.

Read Ephesians 2:1-3.

YOU WERE DEAD IN YOUR TRESPASSES AND SINS IN WHICH YOU PREVIOUSLY WALKED ACCORDING TO THIS WORLDLY AGE, ACCORDING TO THE RULER OF THE ATMOSPHERIC DOMAIN, THE SPIRIT NOW WORKING IN THE DISOBEDIENT. WE TOO ALL PREVIOUSLY LIVED AMONG THEM IN OUR FLESHLY DESIRES, CARRYING OUT THE INCLINATIONS OF OUR FLESH AND THOUGHTS, AND BY NATURE WE WERE CHILDREN UNDER WRATH, AS THE OTHERS WERE ALSO. *EPHESIANS 2:1-3*

In our sins we were ❏ sick ❏ at peace ❏ dead.

You and I weren't merely sick in our sins. We were dead in our sins. That means we are not only unworthy of salvation but also utterly incapable of earning it. Corpses can't raise themselves from the grave.

What a relief to realize that salvation cannot be earned by good works—and therefore cannot be lost by bad ones.

THE DAY IN REVIEW

Review today's lesson. What was the most important concept you read today?

_____
_____
_____
_____

How will this truth challenge you to be like Christ?

_____
_____
_____
_____

Pray, recognizing before God that you are like a filthy rag without Him. Ask God to help you realize that while you could do nothing to earn your salvation, His grace could. Write your prayer below.

_____
_____
_____
_____
_____
_____
_____
_____
_____
_____

The Cost

I once spent an unforgettable day in England with Phil and Margaret Holder. Margaret had been born in China to missionary parents with China Inland Mission. In 1939, when Japan took control of eastern China, 13-year-old Margaret was imprisoned in a Japanese internment camp. She remained separated from her parents for six years.

Margaret told me stories about a godly man called Uncle Eric. Deeply loved by all of the children in the camp, he tutored Margaret. I was amazed to discover that Uncle Eric was Eric Liddell, the Flying Scott—the hero of the movie *Chariots of Fire*. Liddell shocked the world by refusing to run the one hundred meters in the 1924 Paris Olympics, a race he was favored to win, because the qualifying heat was on a Sunday.

Liddell won a gold medal—and broke a world record—in the four hundred meters, which was not even his strongest event. Later he served as a missionary to China. When war broke out, he sent his pregnant wife and daughters to safety. Imprisoned by the Japanese, he never saw his family in this world again. Suffering with a brain tumor, Eric Liddell died in 1945, shortly after his 43rd birthday.

Through fresh tears Margaret said, "It was a cold February day when Uncle Eric died."

Whom do you know like Uncle Eric? It doesn't have to be a person who broke world records or was even famous. It doesn't have to be a person in your biological family. Yet this person has stood firm for something he or she believed in. Against all odds, this person won the race. Describe this person below.

_____

_____

_____

_____

What elements of grace does/did this person show to others?

_____

_____

How does/did this person present truth to others?

_____

_____

At times being separated from home and family seemed unbearable to Margaret and the other children in the camp. But Margaret spoke with delight of care packages falling from the sky— barrels of food and supplies dropped from American planes.

One day Margaret and the other children were lined up as usual to count off for roll call. Suddenly an American airplane flew low. They watched it circle and drop more of those wonderful food barrels. But as the barrels came near the ground, the captives realized that something was different. Her eyes bright, Margaret said, "This time the barrels had legs!" The sky was full of American soldiers, parachuting down to rescue them.

Margaret and several hundred children rushed out of the camp, past Japanese guards who offered no resistance. Free for the first time in six years, they ran to the soldiers raining down everywhere. They threw themselves on their rescuers, hugging and kissing them.

Imagine the children's joy. Imagine the soldiers' joy.

What an incredible story of rescue from a desperate situation. Yet as remarkable as this story is, it doesn't compare to what God did for us. Let's look at some of the ways God acted in history to deliver His people from bondage.

The Hebrew people had been slaves of the Egyptians for 430 years.

Read Exodus 1:11-14 in your Bible. What oppressive conditions did the Hebrew people have to endure?

_____

_____

In Exodus 1:15-17 we read that the Egyptian king ordered midwives to kill all baby boys born to Hebrew women. Two amazing midwives defied the king's order. Risking their lives, they let the boys live.

What reason did these women give the king for letting the babies live? You'll find the answer in verse 19.

_____

What was the real reason?

_____

Because Shiphrah and Puah feared God, how did God bless them?

_____

We know nothing else about these women, but they left an indelible image on history. Their courageous stand ensured the safety of Moses, the one God would appoint to deliver His people from captivity.

Now let's look at a second scene from the time when God delivered the Hebrew people from captivity in Egypt. Time after time Moses and his brother Aaron stood before Pharaoh and begged him to release the Hebrews from their bondage. Just as many times Pharaoh refused.

What was the condition of Pharaoh's heart each time? Amazingly, you can find the same answer in Exodus 7:22; 8:15,19,32; 9:7b,12,35; 10:20,27; and 11:10b.

_____

As the time of deliverance drew near, God instructed Moses and the Hebrew people to mark their door frames with the blood of a sacrificed Passover lamb. God promised that those in each household with blood on their door frames would be saved from the impending death of the firstborn son.

According to Exodus 12:29, what happened?

Was any house left without someone dead? ❑ Yes ❑ No

Finally, Pharaoh said, " 'Get up, leave my people, both you and
the Israelites, and go, worship the LORD as you have asked' "
(Ex. 12:31). Only after his own son died did he give in. Sort of.

God made the Egyptians "favorably disposed toward the
people, and they gave them what they asked for; so they plun-
dered the Egyptians" (v. 36, NIV). Gathering these newly
claimed possessions, their families, their livestock, and dough
without yeast, the Hebrews headed toward a new land and
a new life. Only one thing stood in their way: the Red Sea.

Is a little water too big for God?

**Describe the Hebrews' amazing deliverance,
found in Exodus 14:21-22.**

Several times in the Old Testament, especially in Psalms,
the account of this deliverance is told and retold. In the
New Testament we read about a new deliverance and a
new Deliverer.

Hounded by the Pharisees, betrayed by a friend, forsaken
by His disciples, brutalized by guards, beaten by His inquisitors,
led in disgrace to a rigged trial.

Arrogant men sitting in judgment over Him, crowning
Him with thorns, mocking and disdaining. Beating Him
without mercy, nailing Him to the cross—the worst of
tortures—stretched out between thieves.

Miserably thirsty, utterly forsaken by His Father for the
first time, the picture of utter aloneness.

Hell on earth! Not just one man's hell but the hell of
billions. At any moment—in a millisecond—Jesus could have

called legions of angels to deliver Him and destroy His enemies. Instead, He bears forever the scars of sin, rebellion, mockery, and hatred—the scars of God's grace.

This would be enough for most of us if it happened over a lifetime. But it didn't. This happened in just one week, the last week of Jesus' life on earth.

Think "between the lines" for a minute. What would have been the most difficult act of grace for Jesus? Reread the previous paragraphs for ideas. Write your thoughts below.

_____

_____

_____

If you had time, do you think you could find the Scripture where Jesus said all the suffering wasn't worth it?
❑ Yes ❑ No

You could look for the rest of your life, in every translation, and never find those words! Yes, some of these actions were excruciating. Some were physically painful, but most were also spiritually painful.

The cost of redemption cannot be overstated. The wonders of grace cannot be overemphasized. Christ took the hell He didn't deserve so that we could have the heaven we don't deserve. If you are not stunned by the thought of grace, then you do not grasp what grace offers you or what it cost Jesus.

Briefly describe what it means to you for Christ to have paid the price for your sin.

_____

_____

_____

_____

_____

_____

THE DAY IN REVIEW

Review today's lesson. What was the most important concept you read today?

_____

_____

_____

How will this truth challenge you to be like Christ?

_____

_____

_____

_____

Pray, asking God to show you the reality of Jesus' sacrifice for your redemption. If you've never accepted His gift of grace, do so today. Don't let another day go by. You can receive Christ's gift by praying from your heart a prayer like the following.

Lord Jesus, I know that I am a sinner and that I deserve Your judgment. I thank You for paying the price on the cross for all my sin. I ask You to forgive me of my sin, come into my life, and make me Your child. From this moment forward I want to love You, serve You, and tell others about You. Thank You for Your gift of grace.

If you prayed to receive Christ's gift of eternal life, won't you go and share your experience with a pastor or other Christians who will rejoice with you? If you were already a child of God, what can you do to share Him with someone you know?

_____

_____

_____

_____

_____

_____

Grace and Gratitude

day 3

A poisonous spirit of entitlement permeates our culture. We always think we deserve more than we have. We are disappointed with our family, our neighbors, our church, the waitress, the sales clerk, and the Department of Motor Vehicles. Ultimately, we are disappointed with God because He hasn't given us everything we want.

Read the following verse for God's perspective.

WHO HAS EVER GIVEN TO GOD,
THAT GOD SHOULD REPAY HIM? *ROMANS 11:35*

**What is God's attitude toward someone
who feels entitled to more?**

_____

Scripture consistently reveals that God is indebted to no one.

If only we could see our situation clearly—even for a moment. We deserved expulsion; He gives us a diploma. We deserved the electric chair; He gives us a parade. Anything less than overwhelming gratitude is unthinkable.

God owes us nothing. We owe Him everything. Realizing that you deserve nothing better than hell puts a bad day in perspective, doesn't it?

Christians in Sudan and many other countries who have suffered unspeakably for their faith are deeply grateful for God's daily blessings. But us? We whine and pout.

Why do Christians whine and pout? Check all that apply.
❑ We think we deserve better.
❑ We don't grasp what Jesus has done for us.
❑ We aren't grateful for God's grace.

Scripture teaches us to be grateful, to be thankful, to rejoice.

Fill in the blanks in the following verses.

"_____ in the Lord always. I will say
it again: _____" (Phil. 4:4).

"Don't worry about anything, but in everything,
through prayer and petition _____ _____ ,
let your requests be made known to God" (Phil. 4:6).

A few verses later Paul shared the attitude we should have,
regardless of what we encounter:

"I have learned to _____ _____
in whatever circumstances I am" (Phil. 4:11).

If I grasp that I deserve hell, I will be filled with gratitude not
only for God's huge blessings—including my redemption and
my home in heaven—but also for His smaller blessings: sun,
rain, a beating heart, eyes that see, legs that walk, a mind that
thinks. If I don't have these, I will be overwhelmed with the
knowledge that I have plenty else I don't deserve. And because
Christ allowed Himself to be crushed under the weight of my
sin, I'll enjoy a clear mind and a perfect body in heaven forever.

**Take a few minutes and record some of the blessings
in your life that you often take for granted.**

_____   _____
_____   _____
_____   _____
_____   _____

Imagine a great and generous king who, in spite of his benevo-
lent reign, hears that his subjects have revolted. He sends
messengers to investigate, and the rebels kill them. So the king

sends his own dear son, the prince. But the people viciously murder him, hanging his body on the city wall.

What would you expect the king to do now?
❑ Send his armies and take revenge
❑ Kill the rebels   ❑ Burn the villages to ashes

The king has both the power and the right to do these things. But instead, he offers these criminals a full pardon: "I will accept my son—whom you murdered—as the payment for all your rebellion," he declares. "You may go free. All I require is for you to admit your transgressions."

We'd be stunned—blown away—to hear this, wouldn't we? But the king isn't finished. "I invite any of you to come live in my palace, eat at my table, and enjoy all the pleasures of my kingdom. And I will adopt you as my own children and make you my heirs; everything that's mine will be yours forever."

Incredible. Unbelievable? Then the king continues, "I won't force you to accept my offer, but the only alternative is spending the rest of your life in prison. The choice is yours."

Can you imagine anyone responding, "How dare the king send anyone to prison? What a cruel tyrant!"

As mind-stretching as this scenario is, it vividly pictures God's grace to us. Because grace is so incomprehensible to us, we often add conditions so that we won't look so bad and so that God's offer won't seem so counterintuitive. By the time we have qualified the gospel, we are no longer unworthy and power-less. We are no longer wretches. And grace is no longer grace.

The worst teaching the world offers is that people are good without Jesus. The fact is, God doesn't offer grace to good people any more than doctors offer lifesaving surgery to healthy people. Read Luke 5:31.

JESUS REPLIED TO THEM, "THE HEALTHY DON'T NEED A DOCTOR, BUT THE SICK DO." *LUKE 5:31*

Who did Jesus say needs a doctor?
❏ Those who are healthy ❏ Those who are sick

Jesus continued, " 'I have not come to call the righteous, but sinners to repentance' " (Luke 5:32).

Sinners need to repent.

We are all sinners.

We need to repent.

Never believe anything about yourself or God that makes His grace to you seem anything less than astonishing. Because that's exactly what it is.

THE DAY IN REVIEW

Review today's lesson. What was the most important concept you read today?

_____

_____

How will this truth challenge you to be like Christ?

_____

_____

_____

With a heart of gratitude write a prayer thanking God for the big blessings in your life, like salvation. Also thank Him for the blessings you listed on page 39, such as the sunrise, your church family, and your health. Write your prayer below.

_____

_____

_____

_____

_____

So Undeserved

day 4

Wesley Allan Dodd tortured, molested, and murdered three boys in Vancouver, Washington, 15 miles from our home. Dodd was scheduled to be hanged—the first U.S. hanging in three decades—shortly after midnight January 4, 1993. At dinner that evening both of our daughters, then 11 and 13, earnestly prayed that Dodd would repent and place his faith in Christ before he died. I agreed with their prayer but only because I knew I should.

I stayed up and watched the news coverage that night. Reporters from all over the country crowded around. Twelve media representatives were firsthand witnesses to the execution. When they emerged 30 minutes after Dodd died, they recounted the experience. One of them read Dodd's last words: "I had thought there was no hope and no peace. I was wrong. I have found hope and peace in the Lord Jesus Christ."

Gasps and groans erupted. You could see and hear the anger. "How dare someone who has done anything so terrible say he has found hope and peace in Jesus?" "Did he really think God would let him into heaven after what he had done?" "Shut up and go to hell, child killer—you won't get off so easy!"

Was it fair that Dodd could receive the same grace as you or me? ❑ Yes ❑ No

In our eyes, no. In God's eyes, yes.

The idea of God's offering grace to Dodd was utterly offensive. I struggled with the idea of God's saving Dodd only because I thought too much of myself and too little of my Lord. I had imagined the distance between Dodd and me as the difference between the south and north poles. But when you consider God's viewpoint from light-years away, that distance is negligible. In my standing before a holy God—apart from Christ—I am Dodd.

The thought horrifies me, but it's true. This isn't hyperbole; it's biblical truth. Unless we come to grips with the fact that we are of the same stock—fallen humanity—as Dodd and Hitler and Stalin, we will never appreciate Christ's grace.

You say you want justice? You want people like Dodd to get what's coming to them? Be careful! Are you also willing to take what you have coming? There's a four-letter word for it: *hell*.

Read what Jesus said about hell in Matthew 5:21-22.

"YOU HAVE HEARD THAT IT WAS SAID TO OUR ANCESTORS, DO NOT MURDER, AND WHOEVER MURDERS WILL BE SUBJECT TO JUDGMENT. BUT I TELL YOU, EVERYONE WHO IS ANGRY WITH HIS BROTHER WILL BE SUBJECT TO JUDGMENT. AND WHOEVER SAYS TO HIS BROTHER, 'FOOL!' WILL BE SUBJECT TO THE SANHEDRIN. BUT WHOEVER SAYS, 'YOU MORON!' WILL BE SUBJECT TO HELLFIRE." *MATTHEW 5:21-22*

Now answer *T* (true) or *F* (false) to the following questions.
___ 1. Murderers would be "subject to judgment."
___ 2. Jesus said only murderers would be punished.
___ 3. Those angry with their brother would not be punished.
___ 4. "Whoever says, 'You moron!' will be subject to hellfire."

What kind of place is hell? Our culture teaches that hell isn't real or that if it is, it's just miserably hot there.

How does Matthew 8:12 define hell?

_____

"THE SONS OF THE KINGDOM WILL BE THROWN INTO THE OUTER DARKNESS. IN THAT PLACE THERE WILL BE WEEPING AND GNASHING OF TEETH." *MATTHEW 8:12*

What happens in this place?

_____

Doesn't sound like just a very hot place, does it?

How does Revelation 20:10 describe hell?

_____

THE DEVIL WHO DECEIVED THEM WAS THROWN INTO THE LAKE OF FIRE AND SULFUR WHERE THE BEAST AND THE FALSE PROPHET ARE, AND THEY WILL BE TORMENTED DAY AND NIGHT FOREVER AND EVER. *REVELATION 20:10*

Who are there?

_____

What will happen night and day?

_____

Hell is what sinners deserve. My sins and yours, including our self-righteousness, nailed Jesus to the cross as surely as the sins of any child killer or terrorist. Let's be thankful we aren't getting what we deserve! If God isn't big enough to save Dodd and Osama bin Laden, He's not big enough to save us.

Many think of grace only in the past tense. But grace didn't end when Christ purchased our ticket out of hell. After saying Jesus came full of grace and truth, John added, "From the fullness of his grace we have all received one blessing after another" (John 1:16, NIV). Just as one wave after the next crashes onto the beach before the previous wave is diminished, the tide of God's grace never ceases to bring one blessing after another.

Have you heard of agencies that try to trace people with large bank accounts that haven't been accessed for 20 to 50 years? The money, sometimes millions of dollars, sits there accumulating interest. When the legal heirs are finally discovered, some are living in poverty. All along great wealth was freely accessible to them—if only they had known it.

Similarly, you and I often fail to understand how abundant the supply of grace is. As a result, we live in spiritual poverty. We have now all the grace we will ever need. All we have to do is ask for it.

God's grace didn't get us going, then leave us to get by on our works. Grace not only justified us in the past, but it also sustains us in the present and will deliver us in the future. While we grow in grace, it's not the grace that does the growing. We do.

Several times in Scripture God promises that He will meet all of our needs, regardless of the circumstances. Read the verses below and add the missing words that spell out His promise.
"God is able to make every grace _____ to you, so that in _____ _____, always having _____ you need, you may excel in every good work" (2 Cor. 9:8).

"Jesus Christ is the same _____, _____, and _____" (Heb. 13:8).

Spurgeon said, "Our Lord Jesus is ever giving, and does not for a solitary instant withdraw his hand. ... The rain of His grace is always dropping, the river of His bounty is ever-flowing, and the wellspring of His love is constantly overflowing. As the King can never die, so His grace can never fail."[3]

Perhaps parents' greatest heritage to pass to their children is the ability to perceive the multitude of God's daily blessings and to respond with continuous gratitude. Believers should be "overflowing with thankfulness" (Col. 2:7).

Name an analogy to describe what a life "overflowing with thankfulness" would look like.

_____

_____

I thought of a sponge. When soaked, it oozes with liquid. Even when you think all the liquid is drained, you can usually squeeze out one more drop. That's the way God's grace is.

Jesus said, " 'Rejoice that your names are written in heaven' " (Luke 10:20). If we truly grasped God's grace—even a little—we would fall on our knees and weep. Then we would get up and dance, smile, shout, and laugh, looking at one another and saying, "Can you believe it? We're forgiven! We're going to live forever in heaven!" How could we do anything less?

THE DAY IN REVIEW

Review today's lesson. What was the most important concept you read today?

_____

_____

How will this truth challenge you to be like Christ?

_____

_____

Pray, asking God to help you understand that grace extends to all who repent of their sin and acknowledge Jesus Christ as Lord. A repentant murderer has just as much right to go to heaven as someone who hasn't committed a crime against society. Yet you don't always understand the justice in that. Pray that God would reveal to you through His Word and through godly men and women that from our point of view, grace isn't just. That's what makes it grace. Write your prayer below.

_____

_____

_____

_____

_____

Paid in Full

There is only one requirement for enjoying God's grace: being broke and knowing it. Not so difficult, is it?

In Jesus' day the Greek word *teleo* was commonly written across certificates of debt when they were canceled. It meant *paid in full*. Just before Christ died, He cried out, *"Tetelestai,"* a form of the word *teleo*—" 'It is finished' " (John 19:30). Christ died so that the certificate of debt listing all of our sins could once and for all be marked Paid in Full.

Let's pretend that you sit down one night to pay bills. You never look forward to this exercise in futility, as you've named it. The stack of bills is much higher than your checkbook, and you've just deposited your paycheck. You need to pay your tithe, the mortgage, utility bills, a credit-card bill, the phone bill, the orthodontist for your daughter's braces, and the car insurance for three vehicles. You also have to buy groceries, put gas in the car, and get a well-overdue oil change. These expenses total $3,750, while your checking account has only $2,000. You are $1,750 short. Sound familiar?

At that moment the phone rings. When you answer, you learn that an anonymous gift has been given in your honor, totaling $1,750. You try to refuse it, saying that you don't want charity and that you aren't desperate, but deep inside you know you are. Graciously and humbly, you accept this generous gift.

You hang up the phone in disbelief, but you are immediately reminded of grace. No, you don't deserve this gift. You review how you've spent your money, knowing that you could have been more careful. But this generous donor has given you the exact amount you need.

Things don't always happen this way. But maybe this fictional scenario will help you understand grace and the depravity of our spiritual condition without it.

How do you think this story applies
to our spiritual condition before we are saved?

Spiritually, we are broke, and our bills are high. There is no way we will be able to pay them. We need help!

Christ offers the gift of forgiveness, but it's not ours until we accept it. The offer alone doesn't make it ours. To have it, we must accept it.

A friend told me he had failed God so many times that he no longer felt worthy of God's grace. But he was never worthy in the first place! Neither am I. Remember our wretched condition we discussed in day 1? Grace means that Christ paid for us. All we can do is joyfully accept what He has done.

God doesn't put limits on His forgiving grace. The Bible is full of accounts of men and women who seemed to fail miserably, but God showered grace on them. Let's read such an account.

Read Matthew 26:31-35 from your Bible.
What did Jesus predict Peter would do?
❑ Run when he saw a soldier   ❑ Stand up for Jesus
❑ Deny Him three times
How did Peter respond?

Peter was certain that Jesus was wrong in this prediction. The reality played out in three scenes.

Read Matthew 26:69-70.

PETER WAS SITTING OUTSIDE IN THE COURTYARD. A SERVANT APPROACHED HIM AND SHE SAID, "YOU WERE WITH JESUS THE GALILEAN TOO."

BUT HE DENIED IT IN FRONT OF EVERYONE: "I DON'T KNOW WHAT YOU'RE TALKING ABOUT!" *MATTHEW 26:69-70*

Where was Peter in this first scene? _____

Who approached him? _____

What gave away that he could have been a follower of Jesus?

_____

Peter didn't even have to say anything to give himself away!

Read Matthew 26:71-72.

WHEN HE HAD GONE OUT TO THE GATEWAY, ANOTHER WOMAN SAW HIM AND TOLD THOSE WHO WERE THERE, "THIS MAN WAS WITH JESUS THE NAZARENE!"

AND AGAIN HE DENIED IT WITH AN OATH, "I DON'T KNOW THE MAN!" *MATTHEW 26:71-72*

Where was the second scene? _____

What was the result? _____

**Let's hope for a different result in the third scene.
Read Matthew 26:73-74.**

AFTER A LITTLE WHILE THOSE STANDING THERE APPROACHED AND SAID TO PETER, "YOU CERTAINLY ARE ONE OF THEM, SINCE EVEN YOUR ACCENT GIVES YOU AWAY."

THEN HE STARTED TO CURSE AND TO SWEAR WITH AN OATH, "I DO NOT KNOW THE MAN!" IMMEDIATELY A ROOSTER CROWED. *MATTHEW 26:73-74*

What happened? _____

_____

Now read Matthew 26:75.

PETER REMEMBERED THE WORDS JESUS HAD SPOKEN, "BEFORE THE ROOSTER CROWS, YOU WILL DENY ME THREE TIMES." AND HE WENT OUTSIDE AND WEPT BITTERLY. *MATTHEW 26:75*

What was the result? _____

_____

Jesus didn't leave Peter to stew over his failure. In Mark 16:7 an angel told the women to tell the disciples and Peter that Jesus would meet them in Galilee. The scene is just a hint of an incredible act of grace to come after the Savior's resurrection.

While fishing, Peter and the other disciples found Jesus on the shore. This troubled disciple saw the Lord from a distance and "plunged into the sea" (John 21:7). He could hardly wait to see the risen Lord again. Read what happened next.

WHEN THEY HAD EATEN BREAKFAST, JESUS ASKED SIMON PETER, "SIMON, SON OF JOHN, DO YOU LOVE ME MORE THAN THESE?"

"YES, LORD," HE SAID TO HIM, "YOU KNOW THAT I LOVE YOU."

"FEED MY LAMBS," HE TOLD HIM.

A SECOND TIME HE ASKED HIM, "SIMON, SON OF JOHN, DO YOU LOVE ME?"

"YES, LORD," HE SAID TO HIM, "YOU KNOW THAT I LOVE YOU."

SHEPHERD MY SHEEP," HE TOLD HIM.

HE ASKED HIM THE THIRD TIME, "SIMON, SON OF JOHN, DO YOU LOVE ME?"

PETER WAS GRIEVED THAT HE ASKED HIM THE THIRD TIME, "DO YOU LOVE ME?" HE SAID, "LORD, YOU KNOW EVERYTHING! YOU KNOW THAT I LOVE YOU."

"FEED MY SHEEP," JESUS SAID. *JOHN 21:15-17*

Jesus asked three similar questions. What were they?

1. _____
2. _____
3. _____

What was Peter's response each time?

_____

_____

Jesus gave three similar responses. What were they?

1. _____
2. _____
3. _____

Peter would later pay the ultimate price for believing in and telling about his gracious Savior. Legend says that he was crucified but, at his request, upside down.

Through Jesus, God showed grace to a zealous, awkward, and sometimes unthinking disciple. Amazing grace.

Let's return to where we started. Imagine a slave ship's captain, a cruel Englishman who acquired slaves from Africa and transported them in horrific slave ships to be sold like animals at auction. Imagine that this man later wrote lyrics that become the most popular song of English-speaking blacks in the entire world. Unthinkable?

The song is "Amazing Grace." Some black churches sing it every Sunday. Sometimes it continues for 10 or 15 minutes. Many African-Americans love that song, even though it was written by a white man who sold black slaves and treated them like filth.

What can explain this? The same thing that explains how Christians throughout the centuries have treasured the letters of Paul, a man who zealously murdered Christians. It's built into the message:

> Amazing grace! how sweet the sound,
> That saved a wretch like me!
> I once was lost, but now am found,
> Was blind, but now I see.[4]

The man who abused those slaves and the man who wrote that song were both named John Newton. They had the same DNA, but the songwriter was a new man. He became a pastor and labored to end the slave trade.

"Amazing Grace" moves my heart more than any song I've ever heard. This hymn has been recorded more often and by more musicians than any other. When sung at even the most secular event or pagan concert, a hush falls on the audience. Eyes tear up. And not just the eyes of Christians. Grace is what hearts cry out for! Grace is what people long for, even those who don't know Jesus. Especially those who don't know Jesus.

Complete this sentence:
God's grace is amazing to me because

_____

_____

_____

_____

_____

_____

_____

THE DAY IN REVIEW

**Review today's lesson. What was the most important
concept you read today?**

_____

_____

_____

_____

How will this truth challenge you to be like Christ?

_____

_____

_____

_____

**Pray, asking God to help you realize how amazing grace
really is. As a prayer, write another verse to "Amazing Grace."
Personalize it. Don't worry about rhyme or meter.
It's for you to offer to the Lord.**

_____

_____

_____

_____

[1] John Newton, "Amazing Grace," *The Baptist Hymnal* (Nashville:
Convention Press, 1991), 330.

[2] Frederick C. Mish, *Merriam-Webster's Collegiate Dictionary,* 10th ed.
(Springfield, MA: Merriam-Webster, Incorporated, 2002), 1362.

[3] Charles Spurgeon, *Morning and Evening* (Genies House, Fearn,
Scotland: Christian Focus Publications Ltd., 1994), Morning May 16.

[4] Newton, "Amazing Grace," 330.

week 3

What Is Truth?

day 1

The Source of Truth

This week we will focus on truth. Let's start by looking at the way truth transformed someone's life. Marty, a businessman in our home Bible study, told the group that his boss made promises to customers that the company couldn't honor.

**Check the responses Marty could have made
to reflect truth in his work situation.**

❑ Confront his boss and stand for what is right
❑ Conclude that God would overlook the wrong behavior
❑ Not rock the boat

Our group suggested that Marty confront his boss. If the man wouldn't change his business ethics, Marty should resign.

It felt risky to encourage Marty to take a stand for truth. After all, though a nice guy, he wasn't a believer. We might have reasoned: *Let's not impose truth on Marty. He just needs to hear about grace.*

The next day Marty called me and said, "Listening to the group made me realize that you have something I really need."

So we met for lunch, and I told him about the One who is full of grace and truth. We bowed our heads. Marty repented of his sins and—right there in the restaurant booth—gave his life to Jesus Christ.

God used the persuasive power of Christian truth, graciously explained and modeled by people in our Bible study. The truth led Marty to grace.

**Read the following passages in your Bible
and identify how each one characterizes truth.**

Psalm 15: _____

_____

_____

Psalm 25:4-5: _____

_____

_____

Psalm 40:10-11: _____

_____

_____

Do you remember how we defined truth in chapter 1? Truth refers to the legal demands on humanity that God's character requires and the absolute law He established in His Word. You can see that God's law figures prominently in the definition of truth. However, a commitment to biblical truth is not the same as legalism.

**In the list of actions below, write *T* beside those that express
biblical truth. Write *L* beside those that express legalism.**

____ Sharing that Jesus is the only way to salvation

____ Attempting to dictate your church's worship style

____ Insisting that believers should not go to movies

____ Suggesting that the nominating committee begin its work
by studying biblical qualifications for leaders

____ Confronting the pastor for telling a joke from the pulpit

Anytime we talk more about do's and don'ts than about Jesus, something is wrong. Godly living centers not on what we avoid but on whom we embrace.

The Christian life is far more than sin management. Behavior modification that is not empowered by God's heart-changing grace is self-righteousness, which is as repugnant to God as the worst sins people commit. People who are surrounded by graceless truth are repelled by self-righteousness and are attracted to the world's slickly marketed grace substitutes.

List substitutes for grace that you have observed in society.

The world's low standards and its disregard for truth are not grace. The illusory freedom of permissiveness feels like grace to someone who has been pounded by graceless truth. In fact, people who grow up in joyless religion learn that living up to such daunting standards is hopeless. "Why even try?" they ask. "It's impossible!"

But properly understood, biblical truths are guardrails that protect us from plunging off the cliff. A smart traveler doesn't curse the guardrails. He doesn't whine, "That guardrail dented my fender!" He looks over the cliff, sees demolished cars below, and is grateful for guardrails. The guardrails of truth are there not to punish us but to protect us.

If you are a parent, you've probably realized the importance of guardrails. Give an example of a guardrail you erected to protect your children from a potentially dangerous situation.

On page 57 read three verses from Psalms that talk about God's protection. Match each verse with the concept it expresses.

___ 1. Psalm 25:21   a. Your truth always protects me.

___ 2. Psalm 32:7   b. Integrity and uprightness protect me.

___ 3. Psalm 40:11   c. You will protect me from trouble.

MAY INTEGRITY AND UPRIGHTNESS KEEP ME,

FOR I WAIT FOR YOU. *PSALM 25:21*

YOU ARE MY HIDING PLACE;

YOU PROTECT ME FROM TROUBLE.

YOU SURROUND ME WITH JOYFUL SHOUTS OF DELIVERANCE. *PSALM 32:7*

LORD, DO NOT WITHHOLD YOUR COMPASSION FROM ME;

YOUR CONSTANT LOVE AND TRUTH WILL ALWAYS GUARD ME. *PSALM 40:11*

Revisit those verses, digging a little deeper into the truths they present. Ask the Lord how integrity, uprightness, and truth protect you. Write your thoughts below.

_____

_____

Our God is the God of truth. Read Numbers 23:19.

THE "GOD OF TRUTH" (PS. 31:5) IS

    NOT A MAN WHO LIES,

    OR A SON OF MAN WHO CHANGES HIS MIND.

    DOES HE SPEAK AND NOT ACT,

    OR PROMISE AND NOT FULFILL? *NUMBERS 23:19*

List the four things God is not and does not do.

1. _____

2. _____

3. _____

4. _____

God is not human! He will not fail us as a human does. He will not disappoint.

THE DAY IN REVIEW

Review today's lesson. What was the most important concept you read today?

_____

_____

_____

_____

How will this truth challenge you to be like Christ?

_____

_____

_____

_____

Pray, asking God to help you understand the importance of truth, the real truth, in your life. Ask Him to help you see truth as a guardrail, protecting you from harm and not preventing you from living a full life. Write your prayer below.

_____

_____

_____

_____

_____

_____

_____

_____

_____

_____

Is Jesus the Only Way?

day 2

The most influential theologian in America may be Oprah Winfrey. Her spirituality is a hodgepodge of psychology, recovery, and out-of-context Scripture. The Oprah way is a church-free, build-it-yourself spirituality. All roads lead to heaven. Karma? Sure. Fate? Why not? Reincarnation? Could be. Buddhism, Hinduism, New Age, angel-guided living. Oprah's faith is amorphous, shaping itself to the contours of individual preference. It's a "Have it your way," designer religion made to order for a post-Christian culture.

Oprah doesn't talk about biblical inspiration, human sinfulness, Christ's deity, substitutionary atonement, final judgment, resurrection, or hell. Why? Because they specifically define spirituality. They are truths that refute false belief systems, including the ones championed on her television program.

Oprah says, "One of the biggest mistakes humans make is to believe there is only one way. Actually, there are many diverse paths leading to what you call 'God.' "[1] Oops! Jesus didn't say: "I am a way, a truth, and a life. I'm one way to come to the Father." He said: " 'I am the way, the truth, and the life. No one comes to the Father except through Me' " (John 14:6).

In the verse above, underline the word *the* in the first sentence, then the words *except through Me* in the second sentence. Read the verse aloud, emphasizing the underlined words.

Reared in a culture that calls such thinking narrow and intolerant, even many Christians now consider it arrogant to say that only they will go to heaven.

This notion certainly would be arrogant if we were the ones who came up with it. But we didn't. We are repeating what Jesus said. We are not trusting ourselves; we are trusting Him. If it were up to us, we would invent something more popular. But it's not up to us.

Jesus didn't say He would show the truth or teach the truth or model the truth. He is the truth. He is truth personified. He is the source of truth, the reference point for evaluating all truth claims. That's why if we get it wrong about Jesus, it doesn't matter what else we get right.

If Jesus is the only way, then our lives must reflect His standards of truth. I witnessed this lesson in a startling way once when I flew three thousand miles not to preach in a prominent church on the east coast.

When I was shuttled from the hotel to the church, a Christian leader rode with me. He had been accused of dishonesty and financial improprieties. I asked him about these charges. "Did you really graduate from Harvard, as you say in your messages?" He said he had taken a class at Harvard once, but no, he hadn't graduated. He admitted saying other things that weren't true, but this didn't seem to bother him. I calmly told him that I thought he should repent and publicly ask forgiveness for his dishonesty.

Five minutes after we arrived at the church, I was escorted to the senior pastor's private office, where we were to pray before I preached in the service. When I stepped in, the pastor slammed the door and screamed at me. His face turned scarlet, veins showing. He poked his finger at me. I honestly thought he was going to hit me. Then out of the corner of my eye I saw the man I had confronted. The pastor told me I had no right to do this. "No way will I let you preach from my pulpit!" he shouted.

I tried to explain, but the pastor wouldn't listen. He was aware of the other man's reputation but thought it was none of my business. We went straight into the service. The pastor took the microphone. In a sweet, spiritual tone he introduced the man I had confronted, who then conducted the offering, challenging people to give generously because he knew their wonderful pastor. The pastor then told the church he felt the Holy Spirit's leading to dedicate the service to sharing and healing, so regretfully there would be no time to hear from the guest speaker.

What would you have done if you had been Randy—

talking to the man in the car? _____

_____

being attacked by the pastor? _____

_____

on the platform during the service? _____

_____

On the long flight home I considered how Christian leaders, who should be guardians of God's truth, could have such disregard for truth. This travesty isn't new. Read the verses below.

"DON'T LET YOUR PROPHETS WHO ARE AMONG YOU AND YOUR DIVINERS DECEIVE YOU, AND DON'T LISTEN TO THE DREAMS YOU ELICIT FROM THEM, FOR THEY ARE PROPHESYING FALSELY TO YOU IN MY NAME. I HAVE NOT SENT THEM." [THIS IS] THE LORD'S DECLARATION. *JEREMIAH 29:8-9*

Jeremiah directed these words in a letter to the elders, priests, prophets, and "all the people Nebuchadnezzar had deported from Jerusalem to Babylon" (Jer. 29:1). Several times in chapter 29 Jeremiah spoke God's words to the people, warning them about the false prophets.

Jesus also warned His followers about false prophets. At the close of the Sermon on the Mount He told how to distinguish false prophets from those who are true.

Jesus gave two analogies in Matthew 7:15-20. Read those verses in your Bible. What is the example in verse 15?

_____

How would the false prophets be known (see v. 16)?

_____

Because Jesus' audience was common people, perhaps some shepherds were present. Therefore, the analogy of wolves being an enemy to the flock would have been relevant to the crowd. Jesus knew how to connect with people.

Fill in the blanks after rereading Matthew 7:17-18.

Every good tree produces _____ fruit.

A bad tree produces _____ fruit.

A good tree can't produce _____ fruit.

A bad tree can't produce _____ fruit.

Finally, Jesus said in Matthew 7:21, " 'Not everyone who says to Me, "Lord, Lord!" will enter the kingdom of heaven, but [only] the one who does the will of My Father in heaven.' "

Read Matthew 7:22. Check what these people did, assumedly in the Lord's name.

❑ Prophesy   ❑ Deliver good sermons

❑ Drive out demons   ❑ Write best-selling Christian books

❑ Do many miracles

Why would Jesus reject people who did good works in His name?

_____

Name a modern-day false prophet you have observed and tell how you know the witness is false.

_____

_____

_____

Name a modern-day true prophet you have observed and tell how you know the witness is true.

_____

_____

_____

A speaker can be popular, a sermon can be greatly loved, a book can be a best-seller in Christian bookstores, but all of these can still be full of lies. On the other hand, if we embrace the One who is Truth, we bear the fruit of truthful living.

THE DAY IN REVIEW

Review today's lesson. What was the most important concept you read today?

_____

_____

_____

_____

How will this truth challenge you to be like Christ?

_____

_____

_____

_____

Pray, asking God to help you distinguish false prophets from true prophets He sends. Also ask Him to help you reflect His truth in the way you live. Write your prayer below.

_____

_____

_____

_____

_____

_____

_____

_____

_____

_____

Truth Matters

day 3

Honored historians plagiarize. Politicians invent war records. Coaches embellish résumés. Employees call in sick in order to play golf. Advertisements promise intimacy with someone beautiful if you buy this car or consume that beverage.

We are so used to being lied to and so prone to self-deceit that it's hard to discern what is true and what is not. Look at these statistics:

- Sixty-four percent of Americans say, "I will lie when it suits me if it doesn't cause any real damage."
- Fifty-three percent say, "I will cheat on my spouse. After all, given the chance, he or she will do the same."
- Only 31 percent of Americans agree that honesty is the best policy.
- When asked what they would do for 10 million dollars, 25 percent said they would abandon their families, 23 percent would become prostitutes for a week or more, and 7 percent would murder a stranger.[2]

Once our nation had a moral consensus. Not everybody lived by the standard, but they recognized it. The words of Judges 21:25 seem eerily prophetic of our times: "In those days there was no king in Israel; everyone did what was right in his own eyes" (NASB). What a horrible indictment of the time of the judges.

Do you think the same statement could be made about our time?   ❑ Yes ❑ No

Give evidence for your answer.

_____

_____

Unfortunately, we don't have to read very far in God's written Word to find the ill effects of choosing not to do right. In Genesis 4:7 God confronted Cain: " 'If you do what is right, will you not be accepted? But if you do not do what is right, sin is crouching at your door; it desires to have you, but you must master it' " (NIV).

How did God depict sin?

_____

What happened in the next verse (see Gen 4:8)?

_____

CAIN SAID TO HIS BROTHER ABEL, "LET'S GO OUT TO THE FIELD." AND WHILE THEY WERE IN THE FIELD, CAIN ATTACKED HIS BROTHER ABEL AND KILLED HIM. *GENESIS 4:8*

Could crouching sin have already planted the thought of Cain's killing his brother? ❑ Yes ❑ No
Did Cain do what was right in his own eyes and not in the eyes of the Lord? ❑ Yes ❑ No

Let's read about someone who did right in the eyes of the Lord. David wasn't perfect, but he sought the Lord. In 1 Kings 15:5 we read that David "did what was right in the LORD's eyes, and he did not turn aside from anything He had commanded him all the days of his life—except in the case of Uriah the Hittite."

God promises that His words are right and true. We often find this statement in Scripture. On the other end of true and right we find Proverbs 14:12:

THERE IS A WAY THAT SEEMS RIGHT TO A MAN,
BUT ITS END IS THE WAY TO DEATH. *PROVERBS 14:12*

Death. That's serious.

Years ago on vacation I was interested in taking my family on a boat ride. I learned that if I would listen to a sales presentation, we could go on the ride for $15 instead of $60. All I had to do was sign a document claiming I made a certain amount of money. When I explained I didn't make that much money, the salesman said: "No problem. Just say you do. It's OK."

I replied that it wasn't OK. It was a lie.

"Look," the salesman explained, "these people would rip you off in the blink of an eye. They'd lie to you in a heartbeat."

I was supposed to feel guilty—or at least incredibly stupid—for telling the truth.

Identify a time when you insisted on the truth.

I went down the street to another salesman. Children 12 and under were admitted for half price. "How old are your kids?" he asked. I said one was 11, and the other, standing there with me, was 13.

"No sweat," he assured me. "Say she's 12. They'll never know."

"But it's not true."

"What's the difference?"

"The truth matters. We're trying to teach our children that."

As we left, he shook his head, muttering under his breath.

Tragically, Christians can be as untruthful as the world. Some Christian speakers regularly misrepresent the truth. The names of Christian celebrities are prominent on books they didn't write. Christian leaders take credit for columns written by their assistants. Christian liberal-arts colleges routinely publish doctrinal statements that many faculty members neither believe nor teach. Some Christian musicians take offerings for needy children, not divulging that they retain 20 percent for themselves. When we fail to tell the truth, we fail to represent Jesus, who is the Truth.

Lest we get too good at pointing fingers at others, let's spend a few minutes in introspection.

When is the last time you failed to tell the truth? Maybe you considered it a little white lie. Describe that incident.

_____

_____

Was it right in your eyes?	❑ Yes ❑ No
Was it right in others' eyes?	❑ Yes ❑ No
Was it right in God's eyes?	❑ Yes ❑ No

A lie is a lie is a lie—whether it's in front of your children or by yourself without a chance that anyone else will see your behavior.

I could have saved a few bucks by telling a little white lie in the previous situations, but not only was I trying to set the standard for my children, I was also trying to follow what was right in God's eyes. His eyes count.

THE DAY IN REVIEW

Review today's lesson. What was the most important concept you read today?

_____

_____

How will this truth challenge you to be like Christ?

_____

_____

Pray, asking God to help you do what is right in His eyes, not yours. Also ask Him to help you not grow "weary in doing good" (2 Thess. 3:13). Write your prayer below.

_____

_____

_____

_____

Does Absolute Truth Exist?

day 4

University students, once known as truth seekers, now have minds so open that they don't critically evaluate truth claims. Similarly—and unfortunately—many professors are not truth seekers but are status-quo gatekeepers, highly selective about which "truths" they allow in the classroom door.

Allan Bloom wrote in *The Closing of the American Mind*, "There is one thing a professor can be absolutely certain of: almost every student entering the university believes, or says he believes, that truth is relative. The really important thing [so they say] isn't finding the truth, it's searching for it."[3] Really? Try applying the same logic to your search for a job, a parking space, or a flotation device when you're drowning.

Nothing is wrong with searching. But if you keep searching, do you ever actually get anywhere? Are you ever satisfied?

Jesus talked about two instances of searching for and finding things that were lost. Read these parables in Luke 15:3-10.

What was lost in the first parable?

_____

Did the shepherd take a risk to find the one lost sheep?
❏ Yes ❏ No

What happened when the shepherd found his sheep?

_____

What was lost in the second parable?

_____

Did the woman care about this lost coin?
❏ Yes ❏ No

Check the things she did to find the coin.

❑ Lit a lamp
❑ Waited until morning
❑ Swept the house
❑ Carefully searched until she found it

How did the woman respond when she found the coin?

_____

Imagine if both of these seekers had been searching as intensely for truth. Would they have had the same reaction when they found it? Why are we more likely to tell others about a close parking place in a crowded lot than to tell them about the truth of Jesus? Think about it.

Read one statement routinely said and heard on some campuses: "There's no such thing as truth." Is that a true statement? It can't be. Why would anyone go to college to learn from professors who believe there is no truth? Ironically, those proposing this view ask others to believe it as … truth.

Is this idea contrary or complementary to Scripture (see Ps. 119:160)?   ❑ Contrary   ❑ Complementary

THE ENTIRETY OF YOUR WORD IS TRUTH,
AND ALL YOUR RIGHTEOUS JUDGMENTS ENDURE FOREVER. *PSALM 119:160*

**How do you respond to the statement
"There's no such thing as truth"?**

_____

_____

_____

Now consider another statement from the college campus: "Truth is whatever you sincerely believe." You can walk off a ledge sincerely believing that you won't fall, but gravity cares nothing about your sincerity. We're not nearly as sincere as we imagine, but even when we are, we are often wrong.

Is this idea contrary or complementary to Scripture (see John 8:31-32)? ❑ Contrary ❑ Complementary

IF YOU CONTINUE IN MY WORD, YOU REALLY ARE MY DISCIPLES. YOU WILL KNOW THE TRUTH, AND THE TRUTH WILL SET YOU FREE. *JOHN 8:31-32*

What is your response to the statement "Truth is whatever you sincerely believe"?

_____

_____

_____

React to one more statement: "What's true for you is true for you, and what's true for me is true for me." So if we step off the roof at the same time, I'll fall because I believe in gravity, but you'll hover in the air because you don't?

Is this idea contrary or complementary to Scripture (see John 17:17)? ❑ Contrary ❑ Complementary

SANCTIFY THEM BY THE TRUTH;
YOUR WORD IS TRUTH. *JOHN 17:17*

How do you respond to the statement "What's true for you is true for you, and what's true for me is true for me"?

_____

_____

Even sillier than these ideas is the fact that parents and students invest vast amounts of tuition money for the privilege of hearing similar statements. Is education really possible in an environment that scorns the existence of truth? Facts can be taught, skills learned, propaganda disseminated, and diplomas dispensed. But if truth isn't learned, that isn't education.

**Perhaps you've heard the phrase *absolute truth*.
What does this phrase mean?**

_____

_____

_____

Absolute truth is something that will never change, regardless of circumstance or belief. Read 1 Peter 1:24-25:

ALL FLESH IS LIKE GRASS,
AND ALL ITS GLORY LIKE A FLOWER OF THE GRASS.
THE GRASS WITHERS, AND THE FLOWER DROPS OFF,
BUT THE WORD OF THE LORD ENDURES FOREVER. *1 PETER 1:24-25*

If you have a computer or access to one, type "absolute truth" in a search engine. When I did this, I found 150,000 entries! Absolute truth is not only a popular subject but also a hot topic! Read these startling statistics:
- Only 22 percent of adults believe in absolute moral truth. Of those 36 and under, only 13 percent believe.
- Amazingly, only 32 percent of born-again Christians believe in absolute moral truth. (The Barna Group defines *born-again believers* as those who have made personal commitments to Jesus Christ that are still important to their lives and believe that when they die, they will go to heaven because they have confessed their sins and have accepted Jesus Christ as their Savior.)[4]

Theological illiteracy and unbelief have dramatically increased among evangelical Christians over the past three decades. Churches desperately need a fresh infusion of truth, a vigorous teaching of biblical doctrine. Without it we and our children will have nothing to offer this truth-deprived world.

THE DAY IN REVIEW

Review today's lesson. What was the most important concept you read today?

_____

_____

_____

_____

How will this truth challenge you to be like Christ?

_____

_____

_____

_____

Pray, asking God to teach you truth. Ask Him to help you model and share that truth with others. Write your prayer below.

_____

_____

_____

_____

_____

_____

_____

_____

Truth and Consequences

Today we will focus on an experience I had with my dad. The fact that it's my experience with my dad isn't important. The fact that Christ revealed Himself as grace and truth in this situation is important. If you haven't received Christ, carefully read through the Scriptures we introduce today. You might not be on your physical deathbed, but if you don't know Christ, your spiritual life hangs in the balance.

If you know Christ, regard these Scriptures as a pattern for sharing the truth with someone who doesn't know Him.

My father was the most resistant person to the gospel I've ever known. He warned me never to talk to him again about "that religious stuff."

Pause for a minute. Do you know someone who is resistant to the gospel? If so, write this person's name here:

_____

At age 84 Dad was diagnosed with terminal cancer. One day he phoned, very upset. "I've called … to say good-bye. I'm in terrible pain. I know the end is coming. I've got a gun to my head. I'm sorry to leave you with a mess."

I begged him to hold on. Jumping into my car, I made the 30-minute drive in 20, jumped out of the car, and pounded on the door. No answer. Taking a deep breath, I opened the door. On the floor I saw a rifle and a handgun. Calling out for my father, I turned the corner into his room, prepared for the worst. Eyes half closed, I bumped into him as he walked out. I rushed him to the hospital, where they scheduled him for surgery the next morning.

I arrived an hour before surgery, praying that in his pain and despair, with no easy way out, my dad would turn to Christ. Standing beside his bed, I opened my Bible to Romans and started reading in chapter 3. "There is no one righteous, not even one. All have sinned and fall short of the glory of God" (vv. 10,23).

Those weren't easy words to read. My tavern-owner father had always taken hot offense at being called a sinner. I wanted to gloss over this portion about God's truth, quickly moving to the good news of God's grace. But I forced myself to keep reading, verse after verse, about human sin. Why? Because I told myself: If I really love Dad, I have to tell him the whole truth. If God's going to do a miracle of conversion here, that's His job. My job is to say what God says.

We made it to Romans 6: "The wages of sin is death, but the gift of God is eternal life in Christ Jesus our Lord" (v. 23). Then Romans 10, about being saved by confessing Jesus as our risen Lord.

Write Romans 10:13 below.

_____

_____

Finally I looked Dad in the eyes and asked, "Have you ever confessed your sins and asked Jesus Christ to forgive you?"

"No," he said in a weak voice. "But … I think it's about time I did."

I'll never forget that moment. The impossible took place right before my eyes: my father prayed aloud, confessed his sins, and placed his faith in Christ just before they wheeled him into surgery. To me, dividing the Red Sea paled in comparison to this miracle.

Recall the person you named on page 73 who is resisting the gospel. What would you like to tell him or her about the truth of the gospel?

_____

_____

_____

_____

The surgery was successful. God gave me five more precious years with my dad. The day I held his hand as he died, I knew I would see not only my mom but also my dad in heaven.

That morning in the hospital I had wanted to minimize the truth of human sin. I had wanted to bypass truth and go directly to grace. Yet without the bad news we can't have the good news. Without the truth of God's holiness and the stark reality of our sin, Christ's grace is meaningless.

Read each pair of verses below and counter each statement of bad news with good news.

THERE IS NO ONE RIGHTEOUS, NOT EVEN ONE. *ROMANS 3:10*
NOW, APART FROM THE LAW, GOD'S RIGHTEOUSNESS HAS BEEN REVEALED—ATTESTED BY THE LAW AND THE PROPHETS!—THAT IS, GOD'S RIGHTEOUSNESS THROUGH FAITH IN JESUS CHRIST, TO ALL WHO BELIEVE, SINCE THERE IS NO DISTINCTION. *ROMANS 3:21-22*

Bad news from Romans 3:10: No one is righteous.

Good news from Romans 3:21-22: _____

_____

ALL HAVE SINNED AND FALL SHORT OF THE GLORY OF GOD. *ROMANS 3:23*
THEY ARE JUSTIFIED FREELY BY HIS GRACE THROUGH THE REDEMPTION THAT IS IN CHRIST JESUS. *ROMANS 3:24*

Bad news from Romans 3:23: All have sinned and fall short of God's glory.

Good news from Romans 3:24: _____

_____

Bad news from Romans 6:23a: The wages of sin is death.

Good news from Romans 6:23b: _____
_____

THE WAGES OF SIN IS DEATH, BUT THE GIFT OF GOD IS ETERNAL LIFE
IN CHRIST JESUS OUR LORD. *ROMANS 6:23*

Notice that there is no bad news in Romans 10:13:

EVERYONE WHO CALLS ON THE NAME OF THE LORD WILL BE SAVED.
ROMANS 10:13

Everyone who calls on Jesus' name will be saved! Everyone!

The worst thing I could have done to my father would have been what I was tempted to do—dilute the truth. Doing so would have made it easier on me for the moment. But withholding God's truth from my dad would have been withholding God's grace from him.

Recall the person you named on page 73 who is resisting the gospel. Stop and pray for this person. Make a commitment to share God's grace and truth with this person.

THE DAY IN REVIEW

Review today's lesson. What was the most important concept you read today?

_____

_____

_____

_____

How will this truth challenge you to be like Christ?

_____

_____

_____

_____

Pray, asking God to help you take to heart the verses from Romans that share the truth of the gospel. Ask Him also to prepare you to share these verses with someone who needs to hear them. Write your prayer below.

_____

_____

_____

_____

_____

_____

_____

[1] As quoted by LaTonya Taylor, "The Church of O," *Christianity Today*, 1 April 2002, 45.

[2] James Patterson and Peter Kim, *The Day America Told the Truth* (New York: Prentice Hall Press, 1991), 25–26, 49, 66.

[3] Allan Bloom, *The Closing of the American Mind* (New York: Harcourt, Brace, 1963), 156.

[4] "How America's Faith Has Changed Since 9-11," *The Barna Group Online*, 26 November 2001 [cited 24 September 2002]. Available from the Internet: *www.barna.org*. Used by permission.

week 4

Grace and Truth in Balance

day 1

The Grace We Long For

Jesus tells us of the prodigal son in Luke 15:11-32. The son scorned his father, demanded his inheritance, left home, and squandered all his money in immorality. Starving, he returned to his father to beg for mercy.

What did the son expect when he arrived home?
❑ Grace   ❑ Truth

How would you expect the father to respond to the son?
❑ Refuse to let him on the property
❑ Disown him
❑ Make him a slave
❑ Yell at him
❑ Lecture him
❑ Say, "I told you so"

All are tempting options.
  Jesus tells us what really happened. Read Luke 15:20.

HE GOT UP AND WENT TO HIS FATHER. BUT WHILE THE SON WAS STILL
A LONG WAY OFF, HIS FATHER SAW HIM AND WAS FILLED WITH COMPASSION.
HE RAN, THREW HIS ARMS AROUND HIS NECK, AND KISSED HIM. *LUKE 15:20*

Wow! What a surprise ending! The father dressed his son in
the best robe and put a ring on his finger and sandals on his
feet. He prepared the fattened calf and put on a feast, cele-
brating on the grandest scale. He cried, " 'This son of mine
was dead and is alive again; he was lost and is found!' " (v. 24).

Dignified men in the Middle East didn't run. And they
certainly didn't throw parties for a son guilty of shame and waste.

Was it grace or truth that prompted the father's rejoicing?
❏ Grace   ❏ Truth

Read in verse 32 what the father said about why he rejoiced:
" 'We had to celebrate and rejoice.' "

"Had to." Now that's grace.

Offstage was a truth-oriented older brother who had no room
for grace. Resenting his brother's reinstatement, he essentially
said to his father: "Look at all I've done for you. You owe me!"

Was the older brother justified in his reaction?
❏ Yes   ❏ No   **Why or why not?**

_____

_____

What makes his response more truth-oriented?

_____

_____

What was the father's response to the older son?
❏ "Get over yourself."   ❏ "Everything I have is yours."
❏ "Don't be a party pooper."   ❏ "Don't be selfish."

This grace-filled father responded to his jealous son, " 'Everything I have is yours' " (v. 31). He didn't tell his eldest son to forget it, to get over his younger brother's childish antics. He graciously turned to the older son and said that he was and would always be there for both of his sons.

That's what grace does.

A home full of grace is also full of truth. Why? Because grace doesn't make people less holy. It makes them more holy. Grace doesn't make people despise or neglect truth. It makes them love and follow truth. Any concept of grace that leaves us—or our children—thinking that truth isn't important is not biblical grace.

THE DAY IN REVIEW

Review today's lesson. What was the most important concept you read today?

_____

_____

How will this truth challenge you to be like Christ?

_____

_____

Pray, asking God to help you balance grace and truth in your reactions and responses without compromising either. Ask Him to help you express grace that leads to truth. Write your prayer below.

_____

_____

_____

_____

_____

_____

The Uniqueness of Grace

day 2

Jesus came down hardest on the very people whose doctrinal statement was the closest to His own. The Pharisees were the Bible-believing faithful of their day.

**Read in your Bible the parable Jesus told in Luke 18:9-14.
Check the actions the Pharisee performed
that he thought would please God.**
❏ Lived differently from robbers, evildoers, adulterers
❏ Fasted twice a week
❏ Gave a tenth of what he earned

The Pharisee's words dripped with self-congratulation. He achieved status by comparison, elevating himself by pulling down others.

Jesus described the tax collector as " 'standing far off' " (v. 13). This man felt unworthy even to stand near the temple, a place of God's holy presence. He " 'would not even raise his eyes to heaven but kept striking his chest and saying, "God, turn Your wrath from me—a sinner!" ' " (v. 13).

**Name something the tax collector did
that he thought would please God.**

_____

Didn't find anything? This tax collector had learned that the only thing he could do was to humble himself before God. Many tax collectors in the Bible were filled with pride, cheating the poor out of their money. But this tax collector was different. Maybe he had encountered the God of faith in the flesh.

Jesus said, " 'I tell you this, one went down to his house justified rather than the other' " (v. 14). To be justified is to be declared right. Righteousness never comes by faith in self but

81

by faith in God. The religious leader believed in himself, giving no mercy. The tax collector believed in God, begging for mercy.

Can you imagine the looks on the faces of the Pharisees who heard Jesus' words? I'm sure this parable didn't endear Jesus to them.

Who is another tax collector whose life was changed?

_____

Read about this rich man in Luke 19:1-10.

Because of his short stature and his insistence on seeing the teacher he had heard so much about, Zacchaeus did what he had to do: he climbed a tree.

How much pride do you have to put aside to climb a tree? Maybe that was Zacchaeus's first lesson in humility!

For whatever reason, Jesus stopped and looked straight at Zacchaeus. It's not that Jesus didn't have other people to talk to; He was surrounded by people.

Was it grace or truth that prompted Jesus to stop and talk with this tax collector?
❏ Grace   ❏ Truth

As we find so often in Jesus' life, it was probably a balance of both. Jesus knew the truth that Zacchaeus had mistreated people. He also knew that this little man needed grace.

Scripture doesn't say, but what do you think Zacchaeus expected?
❏ Grace   ❏ Truth

As a tax collector, Zacchaeus lived in a harsh world of truth-only condemnation. But his brief experience with Jesus caused him to turn 180 degrees.

**Fill in the blanks in verse 8 to indicate
how Zacchaeus responded.**

" 'Look, I'll give _____ of my possessions
to the poor, Lord! And if I have extorted anything
from anyone, I'll pay back _____ times as much!' "

"If"? Truth proved that Zacchaeus had cheated people; grace covered him with forgiveness.

Did Zacchaeus wake up that morning intending to admit his sin and to pay back everyone he had cheated? Perhaps he didn't plan it, but God had it planned all along. There are two kinds of people: sinners who admit their sin and sinners who deny it.

**What evidence in your life shows that you have admitted
and repented of your sin?**

_____

During a conference on comparative religions, scholars debated what belief was unique to the Christian faith. Incarnation? Other religions claimed that their gods appeared in human form. Resurrection? Other religions told of people who returned from the dead. The debate went on until C. S. Lewis entered the room. The scholars posed the question to him.

"That's easy," Lewis replied. "It's grace."[1]

Do you agree with C. S. Lewis's answer?
❏ Yes   ❏ No   **Why or why not?**

_____

_____

Our pride insists that we must work our way to God. Only the Christian faith presents God's grace as unconditional. That so goes against our instinct and so violates our pride that humans never would have invented it. That's a major reason Lewis believed it.

THE DAY IN REVIEW

Review today's lesson. What was the most important concept you read today?

_____

_____

_____

_____

How will this truth challenge you to be like Christ?

_____

_____

_____

_____

Pray, humbling yourself before God and admitting your sin. Thank Him for covering you with His amazing grace. Write your prayer below.

_____

_____

_____

_____

_____

_____

_____

_____

_____

_____

_____

_____

A Perfect Balance

John 2 tells about Jesus' first miracle. Wouldn't you expect it to be something earthshaking?

day 3

> **Read John 2:1-12. What did Jesus do for an opener?**

_____

_____

Why? _____

_____

What Jesus did was no great declaration of truth. It was just a thoughtful act of grace.

> **Now read John 2:13-25 and mark what Jesus did.**

❑ Made whips
❑ Prayed in the temple
❑ Turned over tables
❑ Drove out merchants from the temple courts

> **Why do you think Jesus took these actions?**

_____

_____

Jesus' actions didn't emanate from personal anger. Consumed with His Father's righteous standards, Jesus wouldn't tolerate disregard for holiness and truth. With the grace of the wedding feast still in the air, what Jesus did in the temple complex was a striking affirmation of truth.

John 1 says that Jesus came full of grace and truth. John 2 records a demonstration of grace, followed by a strong act of truth. These incidents are startlingly paradoxical. But Jesus wasn't schizophrenic; His actions were entirely consistent with His character.

By balancing grace and truth in our lives, Christians can represent Jesus' character to a world that needs to know Him.

Read the following case studies and mark them *G* if they overemphasize grace, *T* if they overemphasize truth, or *B* if they represent a balance between grace and truth.

___ Benji is late for school because he stops to help someone involved in a car wreck. His parents punish him and tell him that being on time for school should have been his primary concern.

___ Several church members urge the church to allow unmarried cohabiting couples to become church members, hoping that they will later accept Christ.

___ A church begins a ministry to unmarried mothers in which practical ministry is accompanied by a clear call to repent of sin and accept Christ.

___ Edward stops someone from breaking into a neighbor's house but doesn't report the crime to police because he doesn't want the young person to get in trouble.

___ Christian parents teach their daughter biblical principles of purity while allowing her to stay out later on weekends as she gets older.

___ Kate looks down on her Christian neighbor for gardening on Sunday afternoon.

___ A couple listens to a Mormon's presentation with the stipulation that they have an opportunity to share the biblical truth of Jesus.

___ Pastor Tim decides not to address social issues in order not to offend potential church members.

Don't worry if you were uncertain about some of these. You will have an opportunity to discuss them in your small group.

Now evaluate the way you balance grace and truth in your life. Think about your attitudes and the way you typically respond, react, and behave. Then mark each continuum on page 87.

I display grace—

| Never | Sometimes | Always |

I display truth—

| Never | Sometimes | Always |

As Christians, we must learn to say yes to both grace
and truth—and say no to whatever keeps us from them.

THE DAY IN REVIEW

**Review today's lesson. What was the most important
concept you read today?**

_____

_____

How will this truth challenge you to be like Christ?

_____

_____

**Pray, thanking God that because Jesus loved people,
He confronted them with both grace and truth. Ask God
to help you express grace and truth in a Christlike way.
Write your prayer below.**

_____

_____

_____

_____

_____

Better than We Deserve

day 4

Remember George, the university professor I drove home from the theater parking lot? When we met again several months later, two hours before he came to Christ, he said, "I can't get past the idea that someone could live a selfish, no-good life, then repent on his deathbed and go to heaven. It just sounds too easy, too cheap."

I challenged his underlying assumption that we can earn heaven. We discussed the most difficult part about grace—swallowing our pride and saying, "I don't deserve this any more than a deathbed sinner does."

Grace wasn't cheap. It was enormously expensive for God. Yet there's nothing we can offer to pay for it.

**Two thieves were hanging on crosses beside Jesus.
Read Luke 23:39-43.**

ONE OF THE CRIMINALS HANGING THERE BEGAN TO YELL INSULTS AT HIM: "AREN'T YOU THE MESSIAH? SAVE YOURSELF AND US!"

BUT THE OTHER ANSWERED, REBUKING HIM: "DON'T YOU EVEN FEAR GOD, SINCE YOU ARE UNDERGOING THE SAME PUNISHMENT? WE ARE PUNISHED JUSTLY, BECAUSE WE'RE GETTING BACK WHAT WE DESERVE FOR THE THINGS WE DID, BUT THIS MAN HAS DONE NOTHING WRONG." THEN HE SAID, "JESUS, REMEMBER ME WHEN YOU COME INTO YOUR KINGDOM!"

AND HE SAID TO HIM, "I ASSURE YOU: TODAY YOU WILL BE WITH ME IN PARADISE." *LUKE 23:39-43*

Mark each statement *T* for *true* or *F* for *false*.

____ One thief mocked Jesus.

____ One thief rebuked the other.

____ Both thieves recognized they needed to repent.

One thief on the cross asked Jesus to save him. Although every spoken word must have been agony, Jesus answered him, " 'I assure you: Today you will be with Me in paradise' " (Luke 23:43). This criminal would never be baptized, make restitution, attend church, take communion, sing a hymn, or give an offering. He had nothing to offer Christ, no way to pay Him back.

Neither do we.

Remember the king who invites you to come live in his house and be his heir even though you rebelled against him and murdered his son? Suppose you worked hard and saved money, then came to the king and said, "Here. I'm paying you back."

Imagine the king's response to your offer. He would probably deem it ❑ adequate payment   ❑ an insult.

You couldn't begin to pay the king back for his grace. The very attempt is an insult, cheapening his son's death.

On the other hand, some people take advantage of grace, reducing it to an excuse for sin. The apostle Jude wrote:

CERTAIN MEN, WHO WERE DESIGNATED FOR THIS JUDGMENT LONG AGO, HAVE COME IN BY STEALTH; THEY ARE UNGODLY, TURNING THE GRACE OF OUR GOD INTO PROMISCUITY AND DENYING OUR ONLY MASTER AND LORD, JESUS CHRIST. *JUDE 4*

Jude 1 tells us that Jude was addressing "the called, loved by God." Perhaps the "certain men" in Jude 4 were members of their fellowship. We don't know for sure. But one thing we do know: these men were taking advantage of grace, living their lives as if grace had never happened.

Any concept of grace that makes us feel more comfortable about sinning is not biblical grace. It's what Dietrich Bonhoeffer called cheap grace.

What do you think is meant
by the term *cheap grace?*

Cheap grace is grace without truth—a ticket to heaven without any of the demands of living as Jesus' disciple. Genuine grace never encourages us to live in sin; on the contrary, it empowers us to say no to sin and yes to truth. Be assured and reassured that God's grace was very expensive. Yet He willingly gave it.

God has seen us at our worst and still loves us. No skeletons will fall out of our closets in eternity. God won't say, "Well, if I'd known that, I never would have let Randy into heaven!" God knows all my sins. Jesus died for them all. No exceptions.

We are so used to being lied to that we're suspicious of the gospel—as if it's too good to be true. "What's the catch?" some ask. None!

Read what the writer of Hebrews said about God's grace:

LET US APPROACH THE THRONE OF GRACE WITH BOLDNESS, SO THAT WE MAY RECEIVE MERCY AND FIND GRACE TO HELP US AT THE PROPER TIME. *HEBREWS 4:16*

How do we go before God's throne?

The latter part of this verse in the New International Version says, "in our time of need." Never will we be more needful than when we are before God's throne.

Think of the worst sin you have committed. Explain how, in spite of this sin, you can approach God's throne with boldness.

True grace undercuts not only self-righteousness but also self-sufficiency. God often brings us where we have no place to turn but to Him.

Whenever I ask, "How are you doing?" my friend C. J. responds, "Better than I deserve."

It's not just a cute remark. He means it. And he's right. We don't deserve God's daily grace, big or small.

Living by grace means affirming our unworthiness daily. We are never thankful for what we think we deserve. We are deeply thankful for what we know we don't deserve.

THE DAY IN REVIEW

Review today's lesson. What was the most important concept you read today?

_____

_____

How will this truth challenge you to be like Christ?

_____

_____

Pray, asking God to help you realize the cost of His grace. Confess to Him that you don't deserve grace and acknowledge that it is offered to you without obligation. Write a prayer of thanksgiving for undeserved grace.

_____

_____

_____

_____

_____

_____

_____

_____

Extending Grace and Truth to Others

day 5

In your Bible read Jesus' parable in Matthew 18:23-35.

Jesus told of a slave whose debt to his master was the equivalent of millions of dollars. The slave begged forgiveness.

The master had every right to imprison the slave for the rest of his life, but what did he do?

_____

This slave then went out and found a fellow slave who owed him a much smaller amount—one hundred denarii—than what he had been forgiven. Yet he demanded full and immediate payment. The debtor fell to his knees and pleaded for mercy.

How did the slave respond to the debtor's pleas?

_____

When the master heard what had happened, what did he do?

_____

Was it grace, truth, or a combination of both that prompted the master's response?
❏ Grace   ❏ Truth   ❏ Both

"But how can I forgive my father for abusing me, my former wife for betraying me, or my business partner for cheating me? That would take a miracle." Exactly. That's grace.

"Do you expect me to pretend that this person didn't do those terrible things to me?" Not at all. God doesn't pretend that we didn't do all those terrible things to Him. He doesn't pretend that the nails in His hands didn't hurt. He says, "I died to forgive you and to give you grace to forgive others."

Extending grace frees us from the terrible burden of resentment and bitterness. As bad as they may be, anyone's offenses against us are far less than our offenses against God. If He has forgiven us, by His grace we can forgive them.

The scribes and the Pharisees once brought to Jesus a woman caught in adultery.

Read John 8:1-12. What kind of response would grace-only people give to the woman?

_____

Maybe it would be something like "Don't worry about an affair, Dear. God understands, and so do we."

How did the truth-only people in this passage respond to the woman?

_____

The scribes and the Pharisees, experts at truth only, were ready to exercise immediate judgment by stoning the woman.

How did Jesus respond to the woman's accusers?

_____

Jesus rebuked the woman's accusers. But that isn't the end of the story.

How did Jesus respond to the woman?
❏ "Go burn for your sins."   ❏ "Go and feel free to sin again."
❏ "Go and don't sin anymore."

In telling the woman not to sin anymore (see v. 11), Jesus didn't deny truth. He affirmed it by telling the woman that she needed to repent and change.

Jesus didn't deny grace. He offered it. He sent the woman away, forgiven and cleansed, to a new life.

If we minimize grace, the world sees no hope for salvation. If we minimize truth, the world sees no need for salvation. To show Jesus to the world, we must offer unabridged grace and truth, emphasizing both, apologizing for neither.

No one offered grace and truth like Jesus.

Name someone you know who needs grace. _____
How can you show grace to this person? _____

_____

Name someone you know who needs truth. _____
How can you share truth with this person? _____

_____

THE DAY IN REVIEW

Review today's lesson. What was the most important concept you read today?

_____

_____

How will this truth challenge you to be like Christ?

_____

_____

Pray, asking God to help you extend grace and truth to others, showing them both the hope and need for salvation. Write your prayer.

_____

_____

_____

_____

_____

---

[1]Philip Yancey, *What's So Amazing About Grace?* (Grand Rapids, MI: Zondervan Publishers, 1997), 45.

This leader guide provides suggestions for leading a small-group study of *The Grace and Truth Paradox*. Following this brief introduction, you will find step-by-step guidance for conducting each group session.

Learning Goals

After completing this study, members should be able to—
- define *grace* and *truth* as revealed in God's Word;
- describe the way Jesus balanced grace and truth in His earthly ministry;
- identify their individual tendencies toward grace or truth;
- describe ways to balance grace and truth in their lives;
- identify ways grace and truth offer people both the hope and the need for salvation.

Resources

Order in advance one copy of *The Grace and Truth Paradox* (item 0-6331-9755-6) for each participant. To order, write to LifeWay Church Resources Customer Service; One LifeWay Plaza; Nashville, TN 37234-0113; fax (615) 251-5933; phone toll free (800) 458-2772; e-mail *customerservice@lifeway.com;* order online at *www.lifeway.com;* or visit a LifeWay Christian Store.

If couples are participating, stress that each person should have a copy of the workbook so that he or she can record individual responses to the learning activities.

Group Sessions

Plan for each session to last about an hour. Questions are provided to start discussion and to help participants review what they have studied during the week. More questions are provided than you will have time to use, so choose the questions according to the needs of your group.

Study Options

Although this book contains four weeks of individual study, you and your group can choose between a four- and five-session group study.

Four-week plan. Omit the introductory session that follows and begin with session 1. If you choose this plan, you will need to give members their workbooks one week before the study begins so that they can complete their work in week 1 in advance of the first group session.

Five-week plan. The five-week plan begins with the following introductory session. If you choose this plan, you can wait until the introductory session to distribute workbooks because members do not need to prepare for this session.

Introductory Session

Learning Goals

After this session members will be able to—
- identify the topics they will study in this course;
- identify the goals of this study;
- summarize the study format of their workbooks.

Before the Session

1. Provide pens and name tags for participants. Place these on a table near the entrance to the meeting room. Make a name tag for yourself in advance.
2. Have workbooks available for distribution. Place them on the table with the name tags and pens.
3. Familiarize yourself with the content of the study by reading all four weeks.

During the Session

1. As participants arrive, introduce yourself and direct them to the name tags. Also have them pick up their workbooks.
2. After everyone has arrived, welcome the group. State that you look forward to the next four weeks of study, discussion, and fellowship.
3. Ask members to introduce themselves by stating their names and something unique about themselves. Use this time to help participants who might be uncomfortable speaking in front of others to feel more at ease. Limit this activity to 15 minutes.
4. Ask each member to give his or her expectations of this course. Ask, What motivated you to take this course?
5. Have the group give definitions of *grace* and *truth*. Write these definitions on a dry-erase board or chalkboard. State that this study will teach members the biblical meanings of *grace* and *truth*. Present the learning goals for this course that are listed on page 95.

6. Ask members to open their workbooks to the contents page (p. 3) and have someone read the title of each week's study. Briefly preview each topic.

7. Have members turn to week 1 (p. 6). Explain that each week's material is divided into five days of study. Each day's study includes biblical content, commentary, and learning activities. Tell members to complete each week's study before the related group session. State that the study uses an interactive format. Encourage members to complete the learning activities as they study in order to delve into the Scriptures and to apply the material to their lives. Encourage members to complete one day's material at a time to get the most from their study. State that the weekly group sessions will provide opportunities for review and interaction.

8. Ask members to complete week 1 in their workbooks before the next group session. Instruct them to be ready to discuss the information they study in week 1 during next week's session. State that if they have questions while they are studying, they should write them in the margins of their books and ask them during the group session.

9. Close with a prayer asking for God to reveal the meanings of *grace* and *truth* through the example of His Son, Jesus. Ask Him to help us learn how to express these qualities in a way that reflects Christ's character and brings honor to Him.

Session 1
Two Foundational Concepts

Learning Goals
After this session members will be able to—
- define *grace* and *truth;*
- give biblical examples of grace and truth in Jesus' life;
- identify their personal tendencies toward grace or truth.

Before the Session
1. Provide markers and name tags. Be sure to wear your name tag as people arrive.
2. Study and complete the activities in week 1.
3. You will have more activities than you can finish in an hour. Choose the activities that you feel best convey the key concepts in week 1 and best meet the needs of your group.

During the Session
1. Welcome everyone. Begin with prayer, asking God to bless your study and sharing together.
2. Begin by having one member say, "My name is …" Then each member should guess where the member is from. After everyone has had the chance to guess the person's birthplace, ask the person to reveal where he or she was born.
3. Say: This exercise reminds us of what we learned in day 1: the early Christians were not known by their accents, church buildings, or programs. They were known by the way they lived: grace. They were also known by what they spoke: truth.
4. Have someone read Acts 4:32-33. Ask, In what ways is our church like the early church?
5. Review the definitions of *grace* and *truth* on pages 9–10. Call for responses to the activity at the top of page 10 to make sure members understand the biblical meanings of *grace* and *truth.*

6. Say: We looked at several character qualities of Jesus in day 2. What are some of the qualities you listed on page 11? Read John 1:14 and say that we can picture Jesus' character through two qualities: grace and truth. Point out that believers must exhibit both qualities to show the world a true picture of who Jesus is.

7. Ask whether anyone would be comfortable sharing what they learned about themselves from the scale on page 12. Be ready to share your response if members do not wish to share.

8. Ask: Are grace and truth compatible? Are they polar opposites? How can we resolve this apparent incompatibility? Have several members read aloud Matthew 8:18-22; 12:1-8; 19:16-22; 20:1-16; 21:18-22. After each passage is read, ask whether it expresses grace, truth, or both. Answers: truth, grace, truth, both, truth.

9. Mention the challenge of balancing grace and truth for believers today. Ask members to share their answers to the activity at the bottom of page 16.

10. Point out the drawing of DNA on page 18 and explain the analogy: just as the strands of DNA make up who we are as people, grace and truth make up who we are as Christians.

11. Ask a member to read Luke 4:16-21. Ask volunteers to describe Jesus' mission. Ask, How does this mission reflect grace and truth?

12. Recall the author's experiences on pages 19–21 and ask members to identify the conflicts between grace and truth. Read John 15:18. End the discussion with the questions in the final paragraph on page 21.

13. Call for responses to the activity on page 23. Ask, How is Jesus marketed today? Challenge members to show the world Jesus as He is—full of grace and truth—rather than a false Jesus the world would rather see.

14. Ask members to read the daily assignments and to complete the activities in week 2 before the next group session.

15. Close with a prayer thanking Jesus for showing us grace and truth. Ask God to help us learn to show both as Jesus did.

Session 2
What Is Grace?

Learning Goals

After this session members will be able to—
- describe and acknowledge the wretched condition of someone without Christ;
- affirm that grace is a gift;
- express gratitude to God for His grace;
- contrast grace and hell.

Before the Session

1. Provide markers and name tags. Be sure to wear your name tag as people arrive.
2. Get a copy of the movie *Chariots of Fire*, if desired, for activity 4 in "During the Session."
3. Be prepared to counsel any members who accept Christ as a result of their study of day 2 (p. 37).
4. Study and complete the activities in week 2.
5. You will have more activities than you can finish in an hour. Choose the activities that you feel best convey the key concepts in week 2 and best meet the needs of your group.

During the Session

1. Welcome everyone. Begin with prayer, asking God to bless your study and sharing together.
2. Have the group sing the hymn "Amazing Grace." Mention the author's experience when the word *wretch* was replaced by the word *soul* (p. 26). Ask, How does that word alter the meaning of the hymn? Ask members to name synonyms for *wretch* as you list these on a dry-erase board or chalkboard. Read Romans 5:6.
3. Ask for members' responses to the activities on page 28. Follow up by reading Romans 5:8. Stress that Christ died for us while we were still sinners, not after we had worked

our way to our idea of perfection. Grace is a gift, not something we earn. Grace does not ignore our depravity or lower God's standards. Grace sent Jesus to the cross to pay for our sins. Have a member read 2 Corinthians 5:21.

4. If you have the movie *Chariots of Fire,* play the scene in which Eric says, "God made me for a purpose, but he also made me fast." Ask volunteers to describe someone they knew who stood up for truth.

5. State, In day 2 you read about the Hebrews' bondage in Egypt. Ask members to identify ways God delivered the Hebrews. Make the connection to Jesus' deliverance of us from our sin. Ask for responses to the activity at the top of page 36. Conclude that though the cost was enormous, Jesus endured the physical and spiritual agony so that we could experience grace. Ask volunteers to share responses to the final activity on page 36.

6. Ask: Why do we feel disappointed in God? Why are we told in Scripture to be thankful? What should we be thankful for? Ask a member to read Philippians 4:4-11. Say, We deserve hell, but God gives us redemption and blessings. Summarize the story on page 40 to emphasize the magnitude of God's grace. Pause and ask members to express brief prayers thanking God for His grace.

7. Have a volunteer tell the story of Wesley Allan Dodd on page 42. Ask: What are your thoughts about Dodd's statement? Is it fair that he received the same grace as we did? Read the author's conclusion on page 42: "In my standing before a holy God—apart from Christ—I am Dodd."

8. Divide members into two groups. Ask one group to list and report on the hell we deserve, as described on pages 43–44. Ask the other group to list and report on the blessings of God's grace, as described on pages 44–45. After reports have been given, summarize by reading the quotation by Spurgeon on page 45 if it has not already been shared. Challenge members to respond to God's grace with overflowing thankfulness.

9. Ask the group what it feels like to be financially broke.
   Compare this condition to being spiritually broke. Ask,
   What does it feel like to know that Someone willingly
   paid the debt in full?
10. Ask two volunteers to summarize Peter's denial of Christ
    and his restoration by the resurrected Christ (pp. 48–50).
    Emphasize Jesus' grace toward Peter.
11. Tell the story of John Newton, who wrote "Amazing Grace"
    (pp. 51–52). Read the words of the hymn on page 52. Ask
    volunteers to respond to the activity on page 52.
12. Ask members to read the daily assignments and to complete
    the activities in week 3 before the next group session.
13. Close with a prayer praising God for His amazing grace.
    Ask God to help us live lives that overflow with gratitude
    for giving us grace instead of what we deserve.

Session 3
What Is Truth?

Learning Goals
After this session members will be able to—
- define *truth;*
- refute cultural denials of the existence of absolute truth;
- state why a commitment to truth is important.

Before the Session
1. Provide markers and name tags. Be sure to wear your name tag as people arrive.
2. Study and complete the activities in week 3.
3. You will have more activities than you can finish in an hour. Choose the activities that you feel best convey the key concepts in week 3 and best meet the needs of your group.

During the Session
1. Welcome everyone. Begin with prayer, asking God to bless your study and sharing together.
2. Point out Marty's need for the truth (pp. 54–55). Ask: How many times do you choose options besides sharing the truth with those who desperately need it? What are those options?
3. Ask: What is truth? How has your understanding changed as a result of this week's study? If necessary, review the definition on page 55. Use the activity at the bottom of that page to distinguish between truth and legalism. Answers: T, L, L, T, L.
4. Ask the group to identify substitutes for grace found in today's culture (activity, p. 56). Ask members to explain why these substitutes are not true expressions of grace.
5. Ask three members to read Psalm 25:21; 32:7; 40:11 and to describe how God's truth protects us.
6. Ask volunteers to identify the four things God is not and does not do, according to Numbers 23:19 (p. 57). Emphasize that God is the God of truth who does not disappoint.

7. Read Jesus' declaration in John 14:6 (p. 59). Ask members to identify messages in our culture that deny Jesus' statement. Record these on a dry-erase board or chalkboard. Say, If Jesus is the only way, our lives must reflect His standards of truth.

8. Refer to the author's experience on page 60. Ask a member to read Matthew 7:15-20. Ask, How do we know whether a prophet is false?

9. Read Judges 21:25 (p. 64) and ask, Could this statement be made about our time? Read the bulleted statements on page 64 as examples. Ask: What is the difference between doing what is right in our eyes and doing what is right in God's eyes? Who are some biblical figures who did right in their own eyes? Who are some biblical figures who did right in God's eyes? Read Proverbs 14:12 (p. 65). Ask, What is the result when we follow what seems right in our own eyes?

10. Recall the author's examples on page 66. Ask, Why was it important for him to insist on the truth? Summarize that God's judgment of truth matters.

11. Divide members into three groups and assign each group one of the popular misconceptions about truth that are discussed in day 4:
    • There's no such thing as truth.
    • Truth is whatever you sincerely believe.
    • What's true for you is true for you, and what's true for me is true for me.
    Ask each group to use the related material on pages 69–70 and Scripture to refute these beliefs. After time for group work, call for reports. Conclude the reports by emphasizing the Bible's claim to absolute truth. Read 1 Peter 1:24-25.

12. Ask, Why does it often take a life-and-death situation for some people to accept God's grace and truth? Say, Think about the person you identified on page 73 as resistant to the gospel. Ask, Why do you think this person resists God's truth?

13. Read this statement on page 75: "Without the truth of God's holiness and the stark reality of our sin, Christ's grace

is meaningless." Ask, What does the author mean by this statement? Have members read the bad news, good news Scriptures on pages 75–76.

14. Ask, Based on what you have studied this week, why is a commitment to truth important? Record responses on a dry-erase board or chalkboard. Possible responses:
    • The source of truth is God Himself.
    • God established truth.
    • Truth leads people to grace.
    • Truth protects us.
    • Jesus is Truth.
    • Departing from God's truth leads to death.
    • God's estimation of truth counts.
    • Grace means nothing without truth.

15. Ask members to read the daily assignments and to complete the activities in week 4 before the next group session.

16. Close with a prayer thanking God for His absolute truth, which guides and protects us. Ask God to give us courage to stand up for truth and to share it with those who need it.

Session 4
Grace and Truth in Balance

Learning Goals
After this session members will be able to—
- identify evidence of grace and truth in selected biblical accounts;
- contrast cheap grace and genuine grace;
- name ways to share grace and truth with persons they know.

Before the Session
1. Provide markers and name tags. Be sure to wear your name tag as people arrive.
2. Study and complete the activities in week 4.
3. You will have more activities than you can finish in an hour. Choose the activities that you feel best convey the key concepts in week 4 and best meet the needs of your group.

During the Session
1. Welcome everyone. Begin with prayer, asking God to bless your study and sharing together.
2. Remind members that day 1 focuses on the prodigal son. Ask: Did the prodigal expect grace or truth from his father? How did you expect the father to respond? Was his actual response grace or truth? Ask a volunteer to contrast the younger and older sons' responses and expectations. Ask: Was the older son grace-oriented or truth-oriented? Was the father's response to the older son grace or truth? How did the father exhibit both grace and truth? Conclude by pointing out that grace leads people to love and follow truth.
3. Ask a member to read Luke 18:9-14 (p. 81). Ask members to contrast the Pharisee and the tax collector as you record responses on a dry-erase board or chalkboard. Ask: Who did Jesus say was justified? Why?

4. Ask a member to read Luke 19:1-10 (p. 82). Ask members to identify specific evidence of grace and truth in this account.

5. Read this statement on page 83: "There are two kinds of people: sinners who admit their sin and sinners who deny it." Ask: Which was Zacchaeus? How do we know?

6. Recount the story on page 83 about C. S. Lewis's claim that grace distinguishes the Christian faith from all other religions. Ask members whether they agree and why.

7. Ask: How was Jesus' first miracle an act of grace? How was His later action in the temple an act of truth? What do these actions show about grace and truth in Jesus' life?

8. Point out believers' struggle to balance grace and truth as Jesus did. Read each case study on page 86 and have members respond. Allow for discussion as time allows. Answers: T, G, B, G, B, T, B, G.

9. Use the material on pages 88–89 to point out that grace is not cheap. It cost the life of God's Son. Yet we cannot pay for it because we have nothing to offer Christ. He paid it all.

10. Introduce the concept of cheap grace on pages 89–90. Ask members to contrast cheap grace and genuine grace. Record their responses on a dry-erase board or chalkboard.

11. Ask a member to read Hebrews 4:16 (p. 90). Ask, How can we enter God's presence with boldness? State, We are most needy when we approach God's throne because we can do this only through Jesus Christ. Read the last paragraph of content on page 91.

12. Divide members into two groups, assigning one group Matthew 18:23-35 and the other group John 8:1-12 (see pp. 92–93). Ask each group to examine the interplay of grace and truth in its assigned passage. Allow time for group work. Then call for reports.

13. Close with a challenge to offer both grace and truth to the world. Grace offers hope for salvation, while truth shows the need for salvation. Refer members to the names they recorded on page 94 of persons who need grace and truth. Instruct members not to disclose the names. Ask, How can

you show grace to the person on your list? Record responses
on a dry-erase board or chalkboard. Ask, How can you
show truth to the person on your list? Record responses
on a dry-erase board or chalkboard. Encourage members
to commit to show grace and truth to these persons as soon
as possible.

14. Ask members to share "Aha!" moments they have experi-
enced during this study.

15. Close with a prayer thanking God for what He has taught
us during this study through the example of His Son and
through Scripture. Ask Him to guide our efforts to accurately and redemptively share grace and truth with others.

More discipleship studies by

RANDY ALCORN

Small courses. Big impact.

the PURITY PRINCIPLE

Purity is always smart. Impurity is always stupid. There are no exceptions. *The Purity Principle* is a lifeline to help you stay the course in experiencing moral purity.
RELEASES DECEMBER 2004
ISBN 1-4158-2014-7

the TREASURE PRINCIPLE

The treasure principle is a simple yet profound idea—with radical implications. When you discover the joy of investing in eternity, you'll never be content with less.
RELEASES APRIL 2005
ISBN 1-4158-2015-5

Order online at www.lifeway.com or call 1-800-458-2772.